KT-116-951

Stronach

Volume Two

Stronach Media Ltd

Contents

£1.89 (40)

£1

Volume One of the Stronach stories was one of North Scotland's best-selling books of 1992 and spread the fame of the North-east's most notorious village to exiles in the US, Canada, Australia, New Zealand, South Africa and Ireland.

Now comes Volume Two. Here, you'll find new insights into the characters who call Stronach home; the staggering results of a professor's study of modern village life; a collection of the best stories from the first 150 newspaper episodes; more mouthwatering recipes from the ladies of Stronach WRI; a chance to show off your Stronach knowledge and win yourself a prize and, of course, the essential Doric dictionary for those of you still trying to master one of the world's most homely tongues.

Published by **Stronach Media Ltd.**,
Tullynessle, Alford, Aberdeenshire, AB33 8QN

© Stronach Media Ltd.
ISBN 1 897672 01 2

First edition : October, 1993

This book is sold subject to the condition that it shall not, by way of trade or otherwise, be lent, resold, hired out or otherwise circulated without the publisher's written consent in any form of binding other than the cover in which it is published. It may not be copied or transmitted by any means, whether printing or electronic, and may not be stored in electronic systems, or for the purposes of data retrieval.

All rights reserved and assigned to Stronach Media Ltd.

Printed in Scotland by BPCC-AUP, Aberdeen

Cover artwork by Susan Bell

DEDICATION
For Phyllis Walker and Lil McDonald,
and in memory of the late Jessie Stewart
and Frances Alexander

THE GREEN-EYED MONSTER

THE RECIPES

GLOSSARY

STRONACH MASTERMIND

FAREWELL

Foreword

I'M going to take the very unusual step for an introduction to a book by offering an apology. Those of you who bought Stronach: Volume One might remember that the last page, by way of farewell, hoped you had enjoyed the book and invited you to write to us if you wanted to suggest something, query something, or just tell us what you thought of your £7.95's worth.

Having worked in newspapers for almost 20 years, I know the importance of reader feedback. Newspapers ache to hear from readers. They don't mind if the comments are good or bad; they just want to know how the product is being received, otherwise journalists don't know from one year's end to the next if they are delivering what the readership wants. One minute we see our carefully honed prose being printed; the next time we make its acquaintance, it's being wrapped round a haddock supper on a wet Saturday night at Macduff.

It's much the same with books and that was why we included the little exhortation to drop us a line.

We were quite unprepared for what followed. Letters and cards poured in, and not just from Scotland. We had long, long letters from readers in Australia, New Zealand, Canada, the US, the Continent ... and one on QE2 headed notepaper, which proves only that good taste is finding its way to the upper classes at last.

It's interesting to note the different tones from different countries. Commonwealth letters come usually from first or second-generation Scots exiles. Invariably, they have been sent their book by relatives in Scotland, hoping that it would convey memories of home. It seems to do the trick, which is good to hear.

They write kindly of old words and phrases revived decades after they thought they had forgotten them. We were particularly intrigued by the letter from one Australian reader, who emigrated in 1952, and who calls fellow-expats round to her house every other Tuesday evening for readings from Stronach: Volume One, and from the Press and Journal Saturday cuttings sent to her regularly by her sister at Elgin.

"We all get very excited," she wrote. "The kids think we're all daft speaking this strange language that they can't understand, but we have a hell of a time. Then we all fall in a heap."

And it's cheaper than whisky.

Letters from England, curiously, speak even more wistfully than those from faraway shores. One gentleman, from Corby, has not been back to his native airt in almost 30 years, and in a long, amusing and touching letter spoke of his boyhood in Buchan and how he wishes he was well enough to travel back. A woman who had better remain nameless thanked us for providing her with an oasis of sanity while she lived among "the folk that spik wi bools in their moos".

Letters from Scotland, meanwhile, are a glorious mixture of reminiscence, suggestion, sharing stories even odder than the events which befall the good folk of Stronach, and picking us up on one or two points on which correspondents feel we have been amiss. Mostly it has to do with spelling the dialect. (I'm sorry, but ardent Doricist though I am, I can't go along with the theory that it's a language in its own right).

Two or three have suggested alternative spellings for certain words, but the problem with Doric is that it has no great tradition as a written tongue (and, yes, before you write, I except Jamie Fleeman and the like). A tongue with no great written tradition has rarely been set down and has never been annotated, so no definitive rulings exist for its spelling. Losh, there are still bitter battles in the pages of Fowler's Modern English Usage about the spelling and construction of the most annotated language of them all: English. Rules of Doric, by comparison, just don't exist.

So we'll continue to spell as the people of Stronach speak. Doric's strength is its rhythm and lilt and music, which is true of any spoken tongue. And, after all, the stories are the people of Stronach's, so the least we can do is offer them the courtesy of reproducing their words, thoughts and deeds as faithfully as we can.

Which, in a very roundabout way, brings me to the apology that I spoke of at the start of this introduction. For all of you who faithfully enclosed your stamped, addressed envelope, please bear with us, for you took us by surprise. We didn't expect the volume of correspondence that we got, but we intend to provide a personal reply for all of you, for when I write to someone I can't abide getting replies which are only photocopied or computer-generated letters run off a thousand at a time with little signatures that have never seen a pen, so we wouldn't do that to anyone else. *(Hear, hear — K. Barrington-Graham)*

It means it will take a little time, though, so if you're still waiting for a reply, bear with us. Down at the Stronach Post Office, they're working their way through the mailbags bit by bit. It would have been happening a lot quicker, but we hired Gibby Spurtle on a short-term contract to sort the mail. Heaven knows what system he was working to, but we're only just beginning to get it sorted out.

So if you're the lady who wanted Geneva Brose to know about the delicious moistness of her Chocolate Yogurt Fudge Cake; or if you're the gentleman who assures Erchie Sotter that his recipe for Butteries is really a recipe for Dundee rolls, your reply is coming shortly.

Meanwhile, please don't hesitate to keep writing. Every letter is read and valued. *(Nae by me, they're nae — B. Girn)*

Thanks once again for your enthusiasm and interest, and for making Stronach: Volume One, one of North Scotland's best-selling and quickest-selling books of 1992.

And enjoy Volume Two.

NORMAN HARPER
Stronach,
October, 1993

Stronach

A
sociological
study

Stronach

A study of the interpersonal and communicatory dynamics of a North-east village

By Professor Dr Elva L. Fashioned
Department of Sociology
University of Old Aberdeen

IT HAS long been an ambition of several Scots psycho-sociologists to observe, unimpeded, the social interaction of a small community; to scrutinise, in relative anonymity, the interpersonal dynamics of the many small Scottish villages and hamlets as yet untouched by global culture; to deliver the definitive study of that which we might call ... village life.

When the opportunity presented itself to spend two months living in such a village, compiling data for just such a paper for my Faculty, I seized it with alacrity. Indeed, having received confirmation of funding from the European Community Divisional Fund for Minority Cultures, I equipped myself with tape-recorder, pens and a plentiful supply of notebooks and made my way with exceptional haste to the village which had been selected for study.

The chosen community was remote, small and quite unknown; the ideal choice for surveillance. Clearly, my presence there would go unremarked and I would find myself settling into its peculiar rhythms with naturalness and facility. The chosen community was a small village of approximately 500 souls. Stronach.

Arriving at the village unannounced — for to have announced my arrival and purpose of my sojourn would have been to defeat the object of the exercise — I repaired at once to the village inn, a hostelry of no small repute, by the name of the Stronach Arms, whereupon I prevailed upon mine host for lodgings.

The room was small, clean and comfortable (if not especially quiet, thanks to nightly revelry below stairs), but the majesty of the accommodation was of little import; it was this very conviviality which I wished to observe at close quarters.

Having installed myself in what was to become my study base for the following two months, I proceeded to the dining facility of the inn, tarrying awhile en route for a small libation in the comfort of the lounge bar.

It was there that I made the most serendipitous discovery of my entire study period, for I was at once befriended by a Mr Archibald Sotter, a most convivial gentleman, who became my most trusted adviser and confidant. I am convinced that, but for this chance encounter, the course of my studies would have been needlessly erratic and the resulting paper much the poorer. It is important that I record here the debt of gratitude I owe him.

I prevailed upon him to respect the utmost confidentiality of my mission. He understood utterly and, as if demonstrating his good intent, undertook to guide and counsel me throughout; to open doors otherwise firmly shut, one might say.

Our bargain struck, Mr Sotter introduced me to a quaint custom of the area, whereby a promise of confidence is apparently sealed nightly with an alcoholic beverage. He inquired also, if I had any other confidences which required keeping, thus showing me the first quality of a true North-east villager: an innate willingness to help a stranger.

Over the course of these eight weeks, it became clear that there was sufficient material at Stronach for an entire sociological encyclopaedia. Of necessity, I must limit myself to three areas of especial interest, and it is these which we will discuss in abbreviated form here:

1. The Newsie.
2. The Fly Cup.
3. The Spik o' the Place.

Each can be regarded as an extension of its predecessor. From my studies, I have seen that most communication in a settlement begins in chance encounters, usually in the street, although occasionally in other locations such as queues in commercial establishments, bus stops, or merely between neighbours over a boundary fence. This is the phenomenon known generically as **The Newsie.**

The Newsie is merely general discussion of the events of the immediate past, always concerning the community in question. Only very rarely do national or international matters impinge on a newsie. To outside ears, the newsie seems inconsequential, perhaps even trite or banal, yet the newsie is fundamental to good village communication. Where do most villagers glean their information on social events; information of tragedy or upset which might have befallen one of their fellows, or information of great personal joy or success ... ?

The newsie.

Yet for so important a form of communication, the newsie carries with it an implied illicitness. Its practitioners display almost reluctance to admit their source. For example, a husband might ask of his wife where she obtained a particular piece of information. The reply invariably is in the form: "I wis jist haein a newsie o' ..."

In the event that a newsie raises the prospect of further discussion at a length and depth not possible at that particular time or place, one or other of the participants in the newsie will take the initiative and suggest graduating to the next stage in the communication hierarchy.

The Fly Cup is a social occasion held usually in the home of one of the parties involved, although sometimes over tea and cakes in a café, restaurant or hotel. Once ensconced, the participants can discuss in relative privacy the information deemed too sensitive to impart in open forum.

While the. Newsie has an innocence; an air of chance informality, the fly cup is an altogether more structured, more deliberate affair. A fly cup masquerades as sociability, but is the conduit through which much of the hard news current in the community is transmitted.

An invitation to one of these events is to be treated with the gravity it deserves, and is declined only very rarely by its more practised artists, for it is the very lifeblood of village communication. Besides, the participant who declines is very likely to find herself not a participant in, but the subject of, much of the discussion, and no wise villager is prepared to assume that risk.

The derivation of the term Fly Cup is as mysterious as its practice is interesting. It has little or no entomological connection, as far as I could ascertain. Neither have I conclusive proof that "fly" has its roots in illicitness. Mr Sotter has suggested to me that the derivation is linked with the colloquial name for one of the sweetmeats served at these occasions — a pastry square, filled with a sugared concoction of dried fruits and dusted with confectioner's sugar, known regionally as "a flee ceemetry".

Mr Sotter later informed me that it is unlucky to mention the words "flee ceemetry", and that the only known way to discharge such an error is the hasty purchase and dispatch of something known as The Macallan. Curious.

Should successive individual Fly Cups, perhaps involving dozens of different participants in the course of a given period, find common ground in a particular event or person, said event or person graduates to Stage Three of our phenomenon and becomes **The Spik o' the Place.**

One of the most intriguing phenomena surrounding The Spik o' the Place is that the person at its core is invariably blissfully unaware of the fact that he or she is the object of intense speculation, discussion and critique by compatriots.

"She's the Spik o' the Place," is a phrase which carries with it an inherent disapproval at best and an excoriating criticism at worst. Yet, strangely, when the opportunity presents itself to convey such sincerely held opinions to the hapless individual, the practitioner chooses to discuss altogether more innocuous matters.

Mr Sotter informs me that even a chance encounter in the street with a Spik o' the Place is considered extremely unlucky, and that the only way to appease the Fates is the hasty consumption of another of those Macallan things. Curious.

**Dr Fashioned will present her paper early next year
at the 47th symposium of
the Scottish Organisation for Social Scientists.
(Soss)**

What a year it's been

Stronach residents reflect
on the last 12 months

MEGGIE BACHLE

Full name: Margaret Bachle
Age: 52
Marital Status: Unmarried mother
Lives: With son
House: Tumbledown croft near top of Hill of Stronach

FIT like a year his it been? What a stupid question. Fit like a year d'ye think it's been? It's been exactly the same kind o' a year as ivry ither year. There's nae muckle changes fan ye bide in an aul croft at the back end o' naewye.

Ma hens took nae weel in December. Went affa quaet. Nae themsels ata. Stopped layin. I tell ye, fan ye depend on eggs for yer livin, and yer hens are nae layin, it fairly maks ye nervous.

The vet wis real good. I canna afford his bills, like. He kens that. Bit I gie him a dizzen eggs ivry wikk and he looks in by noo and again if I need onything. Nae charge. It's nae often ye get a professional man that understandin.

Well, he jist took ae look at ma hennies and he says: "Miss Bachle," he says. "Yer hens is lovelorn."

I says: "Fit?"

He says: "They're needin a romantic interest. Ye hinna a cockerel here. Ye canna keep hens athoot a cockerel."

I says: "First I've heard o't. This is a croft, nae a bliddy holiday cump."

Onywye, Bogies, the fairmer at the ither side o' the howe, hid a spare cockerel he wis needin rid o' and he came ower by wi it. Michty, what a change in ma hennies. Struttin aboot in nae time ata. Clockin and tickin. I hinna heard them happier. I sweir I could see some o' them smilin. And lay? I couldna hardly keep up wi them. A cockerel surely maks a' the difference.

In a different wye, I'd the same kind o' a trouble wi my Claude. He's been a good loon a' this years. I couldna hiv keepit the croft goin athoot him. Even fan he wis a little laddie, he helpit oot. Nivver complained. Not a myowt oot o' him.

Bit it's nae a life for a young laddie, is it? I ken that. A young laddie needs pals his ain age. He shouldna be labourin aboot a hill fairm day-in, day-oot. Fit is it they say aboot "all work and no play"?

He's 16 noo. Ye ken, *that* age. He wis sittin at his brose ae nicht and I says: "Claude," I says, "is there something botherin ye?"

He didna say nithing. He jist kinna lookit deeper intil his brose and thocht for a while and he says: "Mither, there is."

I kent fine. A mither's instinct.

I says: "Fit is't?" I didna pit only pressure on him or nithing. He'll tell me in his ain good time, I thocht.

"I've got a girlfriend," he said.

What a fleg I got. My Claude. Sixteen. A girlfriend.

Bit I didna show ony difference. I jist said: "I hope she's a nice girl."

"Very nice," he says.

"Will I get ti meet her?" I says.

"I'll tak her roon by the morn's nicht," he says.

Well, I couldna hardly work the next day for thinkin aboot it. I put on a clean overall and I scrapit the hen's sharn aff the kitchen table. I made an effort for the loon.

And what a disappintment! What a like dame! Spik aboot mutton dressed as lamb. Thirty-five if she wis a day. Hair lik cats' sookins. Claes that looked lik she'd sleepit in them. Make-up like cement. Jist a trallop. A *trallop*.

I took him aside and I whispered: "Claude," I whispered, "are ye serious aboot this girlfriend? I mean, look at her. Ye said she wis young. She's the wrang side o' thirty.

"Ye said she wis gorgeous. She's deen up lik a dog's denner. She looks like a pluckit hen.

"Ye said she'd a model-girl figure. Ye could drive a bus atween her knees. Her skin's affa wrinkly. Her face is lik a party mask."

"It's a' richt, mither," he says. "Ye dinna need ti whisper.

"She's deif, as weel."

15

KATE BARRINGTON-GRAHAM

Full name: Katharine Amanda Victoria Barrington-Graham
Age: 49
Marital Status: Married
Lives: With husband. Two children at boarding-school
House: Five-bedroom granite villa in three acres

WHAT an absolutely frightful twelve months we have had. Incident after incident after incident. Barely a minute to catch my breath. And just when you think you're back on an even keel, some calamity or other rises up to meet you. Life's such a *trial*.

It all began innocuously enough. We decided we'd demolish the old outhouse to make way for new stables. We'd been toying with the idea of setting up a small equestrian centre for some time, and Godfrey was becoming tired of jet-setting about with the oil consultancy.

What was our mistake? We engaged the services not of a professional demolition company, but of a former railway shunter from the village. Not only did that Sotter man demolish our outhouse, but he ripped up half our land, flattened the small plantation by the north boundary and smashed all the windows in the house. That was a profligate exercise and a foolish investment, I can tell you.

Against my better judgment — for I am a compassionate soul — I was persuaded to give him a second chance. His next chapter of bungling led directly to our prize Siamese, Suki, becoming ... with child. A perversely huge tom cat from the Bachle croft at the top of the hill had been out on the prowl and presumably had seen an opportunity too good to miss.

Then we were overrun by rabbits. All the saplings we planted to replace the copse at the north boundary were chewed to smithereens. Just little tufts left at the top of spindly sticks. That was when I overcame my reserve and told Godfrey that we had to do something.

So we got 15 cats. Feral cats from the Cats Protection League. They do such a marvellous job. Although, I must say, I was rather frightened by some of them. The cats, not the CPL people. I could see them watching me and I could see them thinking. It's all most unsettling; seeing a cat thinking about you. I didn't like it.

Still, they did a marvellous job of keeping away the rabbits. Provided you were prepared to put up with all the yowling all night.

Then, mysteriously, one day I counted not 15 cats, but 14. A few days later, it was 12. By the end of that week, we seemed to be down to 10.

By the end of the following week, it was seven. A week after that, it was three. It was all most perturbing, I can tell you. I couldn't understand it. We fed them

16

the best of tinned salmon, so they had no reason to wander. Five weeks after we installed them, we had only one ginger tom left.

"Godfrey," I said. "What are we going to do about all our vanishing cats? What could be befalling them? Have they lost their way? Are they pining for something? Is someone spiriting them off somewhere?"

"That's it, old girl," he said. "They're being pinched."

"Pinched?" I said. "Pinched? By whom? Whom would wish to purloin our pussies?"

"A cat burglar?" he said.

I washed my hands of the issue after that. Godfrey has many endearing traits, but he has a chronic inability to treat some matters with the gravity they deserve.

Anyway, shortly thereafter we obtained two lovely Japanese humming finches. Lovely birds. Such sweet faces. And so clean. Except that they wouldn't hum. I went back to the shop in Edinburgh.

I said: "Excuse me, my man, but my humming finches won't hum." He looked at them and said that I should take them home and give the male bird a dusting of talcum powder every day. "And how do I know which is the male bird?" I said. "They're absolutely identical."

"Feed them worms," he said. "The bird that eats the male worm is the male bird."

"And how do I know which is the male worm?"

"Madam," he said. "This is a bird shop, not a worm shop."

There's no respect nowadays.

DOROTHY BIRZE

Full name: Dorothy Mima Birze
Age: 62
Marital Status: Widow
Lives: Alone
House: One-bedroom council house for pensioner

IT'S NAE been an affa happy year, wi ae thing and anither. I've nivver hid muckle o' a social life, and it's even less o' a social life noo. There's nae pint beatin aboot the bush; I've been banned fae the doctor's surgery. I hiv. Banned. Dinna come back, they said. And I'm real sad aboot it.

I liked a trippie til the doctor's surgery ivry noo and again. I liked the company. I hinna really got much company since I moved here fae Methlick. Ma femly disna look near me. Ma son's awa Doon Sooth. I hinna naeb'dy.

So twa-three mornins a wikk at the surgery waitin-room wis lichtsome and shortsome. It helped shove in the days. I liked a newsie o' a' the folk. And the doctor liked seein me, I aye thocht. He seemed as if he liked a familiar facie.

Appeerently no.

It wis back in July that he took me intil his consultin-room at the end o' a surgery ae mornin and he said he wis very sorry, and he hoped it widna hurt ma feelins, bit he felt that a lotta patients in the village were gettin apprehensive aboot attendin for treatment in case they bumpit intil me. He said he wis sure it wisna intentional or malicious, bit a lotta the patients felt harassed wi me there.

"Harassed?" I says. "Harassed? I hinna harassed naeb'dy a' ma life."

He said he wis sure that wis true, bit some folk didna like comparin blin lumps at the tops o' their legs. He wis sure I wisna a lady that liked upsettin ither folk and he thocht it wid be kinder til them and til me if maybe I didna visit the surgery. If ever I needit treatment, I should phone and he wid pey me a special visit.

So I hinna been at the surgery since July.

I miss ma visits.

The days are gey lang noo.

And gey empty.

It's nae that I'm embarrassed or nithing. He's a professional man and he kens his business best himsel. I widna dream o' interferin. Bit he's a young doctor and he maybe disna understand that some folk depends on the National Health Service in a wye that's different fae ordinary invalids.

Ma hale femly's like that. We ken mair aboot the National Health Service and its workins than mony a nurse or doctor, I'm convinced o' that.

DOCTOR

For instance, I've been short-sichtit a' ma days. The National Health Service his lookit efter me nearly fifty year. I canna fault them. I widna tak ma trade ony ither place.

Ma auler brither says the same. He's as blin as me and he gets the same care and he sweirs by the NHS, as weel. Canna see by them. He thinks the nursies are jist angels. *Angels*.

Actually, he gets even better treatment; he's in a sheltered home noo, ye see. And he's nivver been happier. Whist, dominoes, bingo, Christmas denners, parties, sing-songs. And he's still got his ain roomie and a kitchen for privacy. Aye, aul folk are richt lucky nooadays.

Some aul folk.

Bit he taks ... turnies ... noo and again. Nae fine. Well, he's gettin on. Whiles he's as clear as a bell. Whiles he's affa raivelled. That TV jist pits notions in his heid. I get the queerest letters fae him. Ye can be sure that if there's a latest fad or a craze, he's in the thick o't. He saw a health-food programme in April, so he made himsel nithing bit lentil soup and bran flakes for twa month. The matron hid twa Rentokil vans in for a wikk afore they jaloused fit wis adee.

Now he's back fryin bacon and sassidges for his breakfast.

Then there wis that programme aboot nudists. Get the air in aboot til yer body, it said. So he startit gaun aboot in the bare-nakit in his room. Nae drawers. Nae semmit. Jist his bunnet in case somebody visited.

He nivver weers onything else.

Except fan he's fryin his sassidges.

GENEVA BROSE

Full name: Geneva Floretta Vienna Brose
Age: 53
Marital Status: Married
Lives: With husband, Sandy, and daughter, Floretta
House: Three-bedroom cottage in centre of village

THEY say "for better or worse" at the weddin vows. They dinna tell ye how bad the worse can be. It's nae that Sandy's a bad lad. He jist disna think. A lotta men are like that, aren't they, ladies?

The trouble wi my Sandy is he's nae affa interestit in the practical side o' things. If it involves hard work, dinna expect help fae Sandy. He's only got the three interests. His belly. His belly. And his belly. If it's nae on a plate, it disna get a second look.

I blame his mither. That peer woman. What a life o' drudgery. She wis a saint pittin up wi't a' that years. How she managed bringin up a femly like that on the money she got I don't know. I do *not* know.

They'd a simple enough lifestyle. She wis a simple woman. She mairriet a simple man. And look fit they produced.

A simpleton.

The rot set in the day he took early retirement fae the buses. A' that sittin on his backside, day-in, day-oot. He got ower accustomed til it. Oh, he'd big ideas aboot deein the gairden and potterin in his shed and servicin the car. It didna come til nithing. Fae the very first mornin he wis retired, he sat on his backside wi a tray on his lap. I tried wheedlin him intil some handiwork aboot the hoose. Fixin the sticky door til the lavvie ... sortin the leaky roan-pipe ... that kinna thing. He listened — and jist ignored me completely. If I mentioned it again, he complained that I nagged him. Can ye blame me, ladies? Can ye *blame* me?

So I bocht him a dog. I did. Dinna ask me fit kinna dog it wis. I went til the cat-and-dog home in The Toon and said I wis needin a doggie for ma husband; something that wid gie him an interest and gie him plenty exercise.

They were affa helpful. They showed me a lively little thing. Nae pedigree, bit a lotta character. A bittie like Sandy, really. An ideal match. I asked the lady: "What aboot the doggie's parents?"

She jist shrugged her shooders and studied the doggie and said it wasn't very apparent, was it? Well, it wisna. There wis a touch o' a'thing thonder. Sandy said it looked like the faither wis a Cairn and the mither wisna carin.

Onywye, we took the doggie hame. Peer thing. It got affa excitit. Little puddles a'wye. Hidna been trained, ye see. And that wis the day I got my idea. "Sandy," I

said. "I'm pittin the two o' ye til dog-trainin classes. It'll be good for gettin ye oot o' the hoose, and the doggie can learn ti behave himsel at the same time."

It wisna an affa great success. They were at it twa-three wikks and they hidna made much progress. The doggie became a lot mair aggressive, if onything. I asked at the end o' August how they'd been gettin on and Sandy took me and the doggie oot til the back green for a demonstration.

He stood aside the doggie and they startit walkin, then Sandy shoutit: "Heel! Heel!" And fit happened? The dog bared its teeth and went for Sandy's heels. Ye should hiv seen the teethmarks. Sandy needed five stitches and a tetanus jab.

We put an advert in the paper and a couple fae Banchory came and took the doggie awa. Tell ye the truth, I wis relieved. And Sandy got back intil his aul habits, sittin in his easy cheir, nae deein nithing.

I got real narky wi him at the beginnin o' September. "Sandy," I said. "Ye're a lazy clort. Ye dinna help me roon aboot the hoose. Ye spend yer days mollochin in that easy cheir drinkin fly cups, readin the paper and watchin the TV. I'm dampt if I'm slavin here so you can play King Farouk. I'm gaun on strike."

And I did. Fae that day on, I didna dee a hand's turn roon aboot the hoose. The dishes piled up. The larder got emptier. The stew wis lyin thick on the sideboard.

And what a funny effect it had on him. It made him affa ... amorous. Ye ken fit I mean, ladies? He said a commandin woman wis really excitin til a man. And then he telt me a funny thing. He confided til me that black underwear really turned him on.

I said that wis a good job because I'd nae intention deein his washin, eether.

21

SANDY BROSE

Full name: Alexander Clarence Brose
Age: 55
Marital Status: Married
Lives: With wife, Geneva, and daughter, Floretta
House: Three-bedroom cottage in centre of village

I WOULDNA say this startit aff an affa rewardin year. Things were gey slow, me takkin early retirement and ae thing and anither. Geneva's been on her high horse something terrible. Nae a minute til masel. If it's nae DIY, it's the gairden. If it's nae the gairden, it's the car. If it's the nae the car, it's ma waistline.

A bloke needs a little space til himsel, wid ye nae say? He needs a bittie private time til himsel for peaceful contemplation; for rumination, and for pickin a winner or twa.

I dinna ask much and that's exactly fit I get. Nithing. Ma meals wis cut richt back. It's this dietin, ye see. Geneva thinks that if she pits on a pun or twa that a'b'dy roon aboot her should pile in wi the moral support.

It's ma ain wyte, I ken that fine. She wis up in the laft lookin for a paraffin heater last winter. Fit did she come across? There, at the bottom o' a kist, she found her weddin dress. Well, ye ken fit weemin are like if they find an aul rigoot. She came doon the hole fae the laft, face as black as the ace o' picks, and she wis greetin.

"Oh, Sandy," she says. "Guess fit I've found. Guess fit I've come upon up in the laft. I'll gie ye a clue. It's been lockit awa in a kist a' this years. It's fae lang ago and it'll pit a shiver up yer spine."

"It's nae yer mither?" I said.

"No," she said. "It's white and really feminine."

"Yer faither?"

"Ma weddin dress," she said. "Oh, Sandy, help me tak it doon the hole. I'd like ti try it on for aul time's sake. Please, Sandy, please."

Hiv ye noticed, lads, how yer wife gets affa sookie-in-aboot if she's needin a favour, but she's as coorse as cat's dirt ony ither time?

Well, I went up the laft and I found the boxie and I got the weddin dress doon til her and she ran intil the bedroom wi it.

I'm tellin ye, lads. If yer wife finds her weddin dress, dinna help her get it oot o' the laft. And certainly dinna let her try it on. Ye're jist settin yersel up for a lotta misery.

First of a' she couldna get it on. It didna fit her. Nae even a near miss. Well, she's a mair buxom wumman nor she wis 30 year ago. She's got bits she didna

hae lang syne. Bit is that my fault? Is it my fault she rams hame-bakin doon her throat a' day?

Well, she gave up on the frock and she flung it back in the box. Bit she thocht she wid try on the headdress and the veil. "That's bad luck, that," I said. "That's like spillin satt, or leavin fae a different door than ye come in at."

Did she listen? Did she tiddle. She rammed this headdress ower her heid and she admired hersel in the dressin-table mirror. She turned this wye and that, admirin hersel, smilin smiles and grinnin grins.

Then she lookit at me. "Sandy," she says, "Fit div ye think? Fit div I look like?"

"Exactly," I said. "Fit *div* ye look like?"

"Well?" she says.

She wis obviously waitin for an answer, bit I couldna tell her. Ye dinna like hurtin their feelins, div ye? So I thocht for a whilie and, jist as she turned in the mornin sunlight, and a stray sunbeam picked oot the silvery threads and made them sparkle, it struck me. And afore ma better judgment could stop me, I said it.

"Darlin," I said. "Ye look like ye're trawlin for mackerel."

She hisna spoken for a whilie noo.

It's complete silence at hame.

Ye could cut it wi a knife.

I'm makkin ma ain teas.

She disna ask me oot wi her.

She barely peys me ony attention ata.

It's jist great.

AGGIE DREEP

Full name: Agnes Catherine Susan Dreep
Age: 53
Marital Status: Married
Lives: With husband, Walter, son, Sammy, and mother-in-law, Beldie
House: Three-bedroom cottage in centre of village

IT DISNA maitter how badly off ye think ye are, there's aye somebody worse than yersel. I've aye believed that. And now that I've heard fae ma cousin at Inverness for the first time in thirteen year, I believe it even mair.

Poppy's aye been a hard worker. Now there's a quine that rolls up her sleeves and gets doon til the job in hand. Fairly pits her back intil onything she tackles. She's nae feart o' a bit dirt aneth her nails. Shooder til the grindstone, best fit forward and her nose tee til something else.

I dinna ken how she's nae flat on her back wi exhaustion. What a workload she's got. Not only dis she look efter the hoose, bit she's up at four ivry mornin and awa til the fish. Then she's hame at dennertime. Splashes ahen her lugs and oot she goes again, servin in a supermarket for the efterneen. Back for her tea, then she's got a part-time jobbie cleanin offices in the evenins. There's nae mony folk could stand a pace lik that.

Her man hisna been affa weel, ye see. He'd a good job wi the electric, but then he took affa sair heids and I suppose if ye're up at the top o' a pole wi a splittin heid ye could be connectin up the wrang wires or onything. Up in a blue flash.

Well, the Hydro Board jist said he wid hae ti tak early retirement. What depressed he got. It near finished him. He wis aye a prood mannie and it really stuck in his throat that his wife wis keepin him. At hame a' day himsel, wi Poppy oot mornin, noon and nicht tryin ti mak ends meet.

Fit happened? He took til the drink, and that's nivver an answer, is it? Ye'll nivver find an answer in a bottle, I aye say. And he didna. He jist got blootered. Affa sad.

Poppy got him aff the drink. She played on his conscience. Said it wisna fair on her; him boozin a' day and her oot slavin. He agreed wi her and he didna touch a drap efter that.

Well, ye ken fit they say. Fan ae door closes anither door slams in yer face. Peer Poppy. Jist fan she thocht she could see a lichtie at the end o' the close, fit happened? The doctors took her til ae side and telt her that her man hidna lang ti go. There wis nae chunce o' recovery and he jist hoped it wis quick and painless.

"How lang his he got, doctor?" she said. She wis quite brave. She didna brak doon or nithing. Jist looked the doctor straicht in the ee and askit the question.

She's ower teuch a customer for bubblin and greetin in front o' strangers. She taks efter me that wye.

"Well," said the doctor. "It could be as quick as twenty-four hours."

"Twinty-fower oors?" she said. "Twinty-fower oors? This is affa short notice, this!"

Well, she went hame and she broke the news and they baith took a bit greet and snuffle and then they decidit that they'd mak his last twinty-fower oors really memorable.

"Will we go til the concert at the theeter?" said Poppy.

He didna funcy that.

"Well, we could go and blow wir savins haein a slap-up feed at yer favourite restaurant."

He said he wisna affa hungry.

"Well," said Poppy. "Fit aboot if we tak a drive up til Castle Urquhart and jist haud hauns and gaze oot ower Loch Ness and the moonlight?"

That didna tickle him ata.

"OK," she said. "Fit aboot a suggestion fae you?"

He thocht for a whilie, and then he said he wid like to go oot and get a case o' champagne, a case o' lager and a case o' malt whisky. Invite a' his pals and a' the neighbours roon. Phone for twa dizzen takeaway pizzas and get the hale hoose roarin, steamin drunk."

Well, Poppy jist put her fit doon.

"That's a' richt for you," she said. "You dinna hae ti get up in the mornin."

25

MOTHER DREEP

Full name: Isabella (Beldie) Scatterty Dreep
Age: 92
Marital Status: Widow
Lives: With son, Walter, grandson, Sammy, and daughter-in-law, Aggie
House: Three-bedroom cottage in centre of village

THEY think I'm gettin dottled. They spik ti me as if I wis in ma second childhood. As if I wisna here ata. I'm nae mair dottled than they are. I'm maybe bedridden, bit I'm still as sharp as a tack. That's the trouble wi folk nooadays. They're obsessed wi youth. They dinna value experience. They think that if ye're abeen 90 yer marbles get slack.

Nae me. I keep an eye on a'thing. I see things ither folk disna see.

I'd the minister in last Sunday. "Aye, aye, minister," I says. "Lookin for trade? Sizin me up?"

He took a lach. He's nae a bad lad for a young chiel. We got on til the subject o' the Kirk and we'd a richt good discussion. I dinna get stimulatin conversation roon aboot here. Aggie's obsessed wi bakin and Walter's for ever got a peeny on him. I'd be as weel bide amon hens for a' the difference I'd notice.

"Did you have your husband cremated, Mrs Dreep?" said the minister.

"I did that, minister," I said. "I've got him in a boxie on ma dressin table. I ken far he is at nichts noo."

"And what about yourself?" he said. "If you don't mind my asking. Have you any preference?"

"I dinna mind ye askin, Mr Thole," I said. "And, yes, I'll be brunt as weel. If I'm spared."

Aye, I ken the difference atween dottled and sensible, a'richt. Back afore the war — afore I cam ower til Stronach — I took a part-time jobbie cookin in the kitchens at the asylum. What rare times we hid. And what appetites. They fairly appreciated my cookin, a' thon aul folk. What they smiled at my flapjacks.

If ye ask my opinion, half o' that folk shouldna hiv been in an asylum. Half o' them wis perfectly sensible folk. They'd jist got institutionalised and forgotten aboot.

Then, ae day, Aul Queen Mary visited. What a wifie. A' got up in fox furs and a'thing. She met a' the doctors and the matron and then the senior nursin staff, and then she demandit that she be introduced til some patients. She wis like that, Queen Mary. Spoke her mind. I admired her.

Weel, the doctors got a bittie panicky. They hidna expectit that. So they confabbed for a twa-three minties and they decidit they'd introduce her til John

the Gairdener. So they haled Queen Mary doon the lang pathie til the fruit gairden, and there wis John, biggin a little dykie roon the orchard.

"Ma'am," they said. "This is John, one of our patients."

Well, the Aul Queen wis affa taen wi John. They'd a richt good news. She wis interestit in gairdenin and he wis affa interestit in her fox fur. They spoke aboot politics and the Empire and the Fascism in Germany and a'thing.

At one point, she turned til the consultant and said: "Frankly, I think it is a sheer disgrace that a man as lucid and intelligent as this should be incarcerated in an institution." And she askit John foo lang he'd been there.

"I'm sivventy-six, my lady," he said. "And I've been in here since I wis nine."

What a shock Queen Mary got. She wis furious. "We'll see about that," she said. "As soon as I am back in London I will be contacting Mr Baldwin and have you discharged at once. Why, you're one of the most lucid people I have met."

Well, John got affa emotional, thinkin that the Queen wis concerned for him. He got affa excitit. "Wid ye?" he said. "Wid ye really dee that for me?"

"Of course I shall," said the Queen, and she marched back up the pathie, trailin the doctors ahen her and mutterin and complainin aboot the dreadful treatment o' an innocent human bein.

Then a brick fussled through the air and hit her — CRACK — on the back o' the heid.

She pickit hersel up. She wis dazed and a' thing. And there wis John the Gairdener, smilin. And he shoutit:

"Dinna forget now!"

WALTER DREEP

Full name: Walter Aloysius Arthur Dreep
Age: 64
Marital Status: Married
Lives: With wife, Aggie, son, Sammy, and mother, Beldie
House: Three-bedroom cottage in centre of village

IT HISNA been an affa good year. First of a' the pound crashed in Black Wednesday and there wis consternation in a' the money markets. Then the Chancellor o' the Exchequer announced that the country wis £50billion short and we'd a' hae ti tichten wir belts and show a stiff upper lip. And then they stopped makkin traditional Fairy Liquid. It wis the last straw. I wis that mad. That lemon-scented stuff disna agree wi my hands. And what a stink it gies yer plates. Atween that and Fairy Snow in different boxes, I dinna ken if I'm comin or goin.

We didna hae a holiday this year. Aggie says we should save and go and see her relations in Canada next year. So we jist went days here and there. It wis fine enough. Aggie wid pack a picnic and a flask and aff we wid set. The great thing aboot a holiday lik that is ye've nae chase. There's nae pressure. Ye can go as ye please, far ye please.

We went ower The Lecht ae day. That wisna an affa happy experience. We took wir picnic and we stoppit in a layby on the Tamintoul side. A bonnie sunny day and a'thing. And I jist says til Aggie: "Aggie," I says. "I dinna ken why folk goes abroad their holidays fan we've scenery lik this at hame."

She says: "Come here and eat yer softies, ye feel gype." There's nae a lotta romance in my Aggie.

Onywye, she'd put Sandwich Spread in the softies. Ye ken, little crunchy boolies in salad cream. Well, they were tasty enough gaun doon. The trouble wis, The Lecht's an affa up-and-doonie kinna road. Affa howps and hallas. We'd hardly reached the top on wir road hame and baith the twa o's wis green. Bricht green. We jist hid time ti draw in aboot the ski centre car park and BOWF!

What sick we were. And ye ken this? Sandwich Spread's the only thing I've come across that looks and tastes the same gaun doon and comin back up.

Of course, that hisna been ma only trial. Well, tell ye the truth, Aggie and me, we hinna been exactly cosy and lovey-dovey recently. I dinna ken fit it is. Ae minute she's happy as larry. The next, she doon in the dumps.

Sandy Brose tells me it must be the change o' life. "Fit symptoms am I lookin oot for?" I askit him. "Well," he says, "she'll be ill-natered ae minute and fu o' the joys the next. She'll be affa easy rattled. She'll bite yer heid aff wi nae

warnin. She'll shout and bawl at ye and ca ye a' the coorse names under the sun."

I says: "In that case, Sandy, I doot she's been gaun through the change o' life since 1953. Will I phone the Guinness Booka Records?"

Honestly, I've tried a'thing. I've tried ignorin her bad moods and hopin she'll win her wye oot o' them naturally. I've tried sympathisin, but she jist bites ma heid aff. And I've tried jokin and haein a bit lach wi her. That wis the worst idea o' the lot.

Fan my Aggie's depressed, ye see, she goes up til her wardrobe and tries on maybe a twa-three outfits she hisna hid on for a whilie, jist ti keep her occupied, ye understand; tak her mind aff her worries.

So this day she came doon the stairs and she'd a face on her lik thunder. I says til masel: "Aye, Walter," I says. "Ye're on eggshells noo, chummie. Watch yersel. Dinna get ower serious wi her. Be licht-hertit. Be shortsome. Be a bittie devil-may-care."

So she comes through til the kitchen. Now, she kens I dinna like onyb'dy else roon aboot me fan I'm ironin, bit she came in fitivver. I didna say onything.

She wis weerin this great big hat. A great big floppy thing. The last time I saw it wis a weddin dance at Torphins in 1978 and it didna look affa great then.

Onywye, she says, fae oot aneth this great big hat: "Walter," she says. "I hinna been masel lately. I've been doon in the dumps."

And I says: "Is that far ye got yer hat?"

Now, lads, you ken. It wis jist a joke.

What a time it took ti find the Elastoplast.

BABBIE GIRN

Full name: Barbara Florentyna McTavish Girn
Age: 68
Marital Status: Widow
Lives: Alone
House: Terrace in middle of village

THE autumn wisna very good. The rain nivver haltit. Days and days o' hale watter. And what windy. An affa amount o' leaves. Leaves a'wye. Blockit a' ma drains. Couldna move for watter. I hinna seen floods like it. I phoned the cooncil, and a very nice lady said they'd been inundated wi calls. The hale village wis the same. Could I wait a coupla days?

I says: "Lassie," I says. "I'm nae gaun onywye unless ye send a boat. I'll jist bide far I am."

It wis funny, though. Ye dinna appreciate gettin oot and aboot until ye're housebound. I widna like ti be an invalid. I like bein oot and aboot. Seein things. Seein folk. Ye canna dee that fan ye're strandit in yer hoose.

So I tried pittin ma time til good use. I listened til the radio. I read books. I did ma knittin. Then I thocht: "Babbie," I thocht. "Improve yersel. Ye're nae ower aul ti pick up a new skill. Aul dogs *can* learn new tricks."

It so happened that I'd a bookie fae the library aboot first aid. I'd aye been meanin ti learn aboot first aid. Ivver since that wifie collapsed at the bus stop three year ago; crackit her heid aff the dyke, and split open her leg. A tin o' syrup fell oot o' her message-bag and landit on ma feet. What sair feet I hid. I'm sure if I'd kent first aid I widna hiv hid feet half as sair as thon.

So I studied the bookie, and I practised wi dusters on ma tailor's dummy. Though I say it masel, I got real good wi the bandages. I'd the dummy strappit up in nae time ata. Bonnie clean knots and a'thing. There's nithing like self-improvement for giein ye a golden glow o' satisfaction.

Spikkin aboot golden glows o' satisfaction; nae lang afore the floods, I'd ma niece, Ambrosia, fae the Broch, ower for a visit and she wis tellin me aboot her grandfather. She'd gone roon by ae day for her usual visit and a fly cup and the aul man wis standin in front o' the mirror abeen the fireplace, tyin his Sunday-best tie.

"Michty, granda," she said. "Far are ye gaun?"

"Canna stop the day, quine," he said. "Canna stop. I'm awa til a weddin."

"A weddin?" she says. "Fa's weddin?"

"Ma pal Jimmy," said her granda.

"Bit Jimmy's ninety-six," she said. "Ninety-six and he's gettin mairriet?"

"Getting mairriet," said the grandfather. "Til a young thing o' twinty-six. Great lang legs. Blonde hair and bonnie blue een. Her faither's a skipper wi twa boats."

"Michty," said Ambrosia. "Fit dis a man o' ninety-six wint ti get mairriet for?"

"He disna *wint* ti get mairriet," said granda. "He *his* ti get mairriet."

It must be something in a' that fish they eat at the Broch.

Onywye, nae lang efter that the floods came and I wis strandit, so I hinna heard nae mair aboot Ambrosia's granda's pal and his young bride.

Bit fit div ye think? Fit *div* ye think?

I aye say there's a reason for a'thing. Wir fates is a' set oot for us on some big chart on the Pearly Gates.

Nae seener hid I finished studyin ma first-aid book than I peeps oot ma windi ti see if the rain wis aff. And fit did I see?

I saw a man collapsed against ma wa. Collapsed. Jist lyin there. Flat oot. On the grun. Face doon.

I didna panic. I says til masel: "Babbie," I says. "Dinna panic. Ye ken fit ye maun dee. Ye're weel-trained in first aid."

I rippit the travellin-rug aff the back o' ma sofa and I raced oot the front door. I flung the rug ower the top o' him. I turned him ontil his back. I grippit his nose and I gave him the kissa life. Nae bother. I jist put ma moo ower his and I huffit and puffit for a' I wis worth.

Then I stood back and lookit at him. He seemed kinna dazed.

"Wifie," he says. "I ken ye're pleased ti see me.

"Bit I'm only unblockin yer drains."

EBENEZER GRIP

Full name: Ebenezer Jacob Scrooge Grip
Age: 93
Marital Status: Widower
Lives: Alone
House: Two-bedroom flat above village shop

WHAT a year it's been for moochers and panhandlers. They say it's the recession, bit I think folk in this country hiv lost the will for an honest day's labours. They expect life handit til them on a plate. They think the country owes them a livin. They sit on their backsides a' day, lookin for excuses, blamin ither folk. If they got aff their backsides and lookit for work instead o' feelin sorry for themsels, I'd hae a lot mair time for their problems.

(I widna really, of course, for I'm nae interestit in ither folk's problems. It's their problems and they're welcome til them).

Bit they come roon by the Emporium lookin for tick and bargains and money aff. I aye say no. Better nae gettin startit on that sorta capers. It's a slippery slope, that. I aye say: "I'm sorry (although I'm nae really). I'm sorry, but I can't run ma business lik a charity. If I ran ma business lik a charity I'd be oot on ma uppers in nae time ata, and then far wid I be?"

"Ye'd be the same as us," they say.

Gey lippy folk, the hard-up.

Onywye, I've noticed a new trend. You company lads'll ken a' aboot this.

Corporate charity, it's ca'ed.

They send roon clean-cut folk. Usually middle-aged wifies or young lads in sharp black suits and short hair. They tell ye a' aboot the problems o' the world and then they pump ye for siller. I think it's a disgrace. It's playin on folk's guilt and it shouldna be allowed. It's a bittie lik a' that collectin cans bein rattled aneth yer neb in Union Street on a Setterday. A dampt liberty.

Onywye, this charity folk comes breezin intil yer shop, a' clipboards and brief-cases, and ye say: "Can I help ye?"

Their answer's aye the same. "Perhaps," they say, "but I can certainly help you." And ye ken fine ye've anither dampt moocher in yer shop.

"I'm nae interestit," ye say. "I gave five year ago." Do they listen? Of coorse they dinna. They stand there as if ye'd nae said onything and they start their little speeches aboot compassion, and the trials and tribulations o' the warld and how ither folk's a lot less fortunate than yersel.

I say: "If the ither folk got aff their erses and did a hand's turn they widna need charity." In ae lug and oot the ither. Nae effect at a'.

I'd a wifie in here in April. It didna maitter fit I said, she went on and on wi this little speech aboot folk bein depressed wi unemployment and how jist a small regular donation fae successful businesspeople lik masel wid dee the trick. Could she pit me doon for ten poun a month? Maybe twinty, as I obviously had known success in ma time?

I says: "Wifie," I says, "d'ye think yer peer, hard-up sowels are the only folk that hiv kent hardship and sair herts? Ye think I hinna been throwe the mill in ma time? Ye think I hinna faced up til adversity and sorrow?"

It wis the first time she'd shut up in quarter o' an oor.

I said: "Let me tell you that I hid a mother that wis near destitute. Nae visible means o' support. Endit her days in a home for women of nae substance.

"Let me tell you that I hid a brither that wis invalided in the first war. Gassed, and came hame a physical wreck. Needit care and attention twinty-fower oors a day, bit he couldna get it and he endit his life in a serviceman's home.

"Let me tell ye aboot ma sister's man bein killed in an explosion at his work, leavin her wi fower kiddies til look efter and nae job. In jist a few seconds, that kiddies' lives wis ruined — afore their lives even got startit.

"Ye see fit I mean?"

Well, she lookit gey sheepish. I dinna think onybody hid ivver spoken til her like that afore.

"I think I see what you mean," she says.

"Exactly," I says.

"And if *they* got nithing oot o' me, you and yer charity certainly winna."

VIRGINIA HUFFIE

Full name: Virginia Margaret Mary Huffie
Age: 67
Marital Status: Spinster
Lives: Alone
House: Terrace in middle of village

ACTUALLY, it's been quite a sad year for me. My cousin Davie, fae Auchterless, took a turnie in his gairden in June. Twa days later, I saw his death in the paper. What a shock. I wis jist lookin at the Personal Messages and there it wis. David Huffie. Ma cousin. Deid.

Babbie wis affa good. Affa sympathetic, in her ain wye. She came next door and she says: "I see fae the paper ye'll hae a funeral in twa-three days. I'll mak up a plate o' sandwiches."

"Babbie," I said. "The funeral's at Auchterless. I winna need nae sandwiches." Bit she widna hear o't. "Na," she said. "Ye'll tak sandwiches. Ye canna hae ower mony sandwiches at a funeral. Softies or loaf? Fittiver's nae aeten ye can tak hame. Will I mak up a twa-three jeelies?"

He'd taen turnies afore. There wis the time in 1983 he wis at death's door for three wikks. He recovered, though. Back fit as a fiddle. What mad his hoose-keeper wis. She'd bocht the biled ham for the funeral and a'thing.

And now he's awa for good this time. I didna sleep weel that first nicht for thinkin o' the good times Davie and me hid on holiday as kids. We didna go far. Dunbar wis the end o' the earth til us, bit what happy we were. Oot on the sands wi buckets and spads. Happy as onything. We didna ken onything else, ye see.

Davie collected buckies on the beach and selt them til the Dunbar fishman. I think Davie must be the only person I ever came across that went on his holidays and come hame wi mair siller than he went awa wi.

He wis aye a bit o' an entrepreneur, Davie. He aye hid an eye for siller. It wis a foregone conclusion that he wid set up his ain business and mak his pile. It took him a whilie, though. His faither wis for ever askin him fit he wid dee for a career and Davie wid jist smile and say: "Empires isna built in a day."

And his faither wid say: "Maybe no. And if ye dinna get aff yer erse, ye winna be biggin ony empires ata." He'd aye a wye wi words, Uncle Geordie.

Then Davie wis at the mart at Kittybrewster ae Friday and a thocht struck him. Carrots.

Yes, carrots. He saw a gap in the market that wisna filled and he seized it. It wis the makkin o' him. He set up a carrot firm and he got a contract supplyin North-east carrots til the top restaurants in London.

34

By the time he wis 30, he wis nearly a millionaire. A great big hoose at Turriff. Three-fower fairms. A carrot-processin factory. Ninety staff. And the money wis jist rollin in. He branched oot til Europe in the 1960s.

And then the beggin letters startit. Isn't it amazin how relatives ye didna ken ye'd got suddenly show up for aul time's sake if they get a sniff o' siller?

Davie wis wise til them, though. He wis a crafty devil. Not one o' them got a penny oot o' him. He aye left them wi jist that hope that there micht be something some day. Jist a hint.

So they fussed aboot him and a'thing. Fan he retired til his ranch at Auchterless, they papered his hoose and did the flittin. They dug his gairden and pluntit trees. They took his dogs for walks. They did his messages. They did a' his cookin. And they did it a' for nithing, on a promise o' a mention in his will.

And now Davie's deid.

Awa fae't a'.

He wis a bachelor til the day he slippit awa. Nivver mairriet. Nivver hid the time. Ower busy amon carrots, I suppose.

So a' the hingers-on turned up til the readin o' the will. Ye could see them slaverin at the thocht o' their years o' investment maturin at last.

"There's 10,000 for Jeems," said the solicitor, readin oot Davie's handwritin. "There's 10,000 for Mary. And 10,000 for Wullie. As for Minnie, she gets 20,000."

What excitit they a' were.

Until they found oot it wis carrots.

ERCHIE SOTTER

Full name: Archibald Stott Sotter
Age: 76
Marital Status: Widower
Lives: Alone
House: Terraced house in middle of village

I'VE been in dispute wi the council near the hale o' this past year. They dinna look efter cooncil hooses affa weel nooadays. They're nae interestit. Ye phone them and the phone rings and rings and rings. If it *is* answered, ye usually get somebody that disna ken spit. I've washed ma hands o' them.

It a' startit the day their buildins inspector came roon aboot. He'd got his little identity card and a'thing and I says: "How div I ken you're a richt buildins inspector and nae some shifty blighter?" He says: "Because I've got ma card."

I says: "Ye've got a card, bit how div I ken it's a genuine card? Ye could hiv bocht that card fae a novelty shop for a' I ken."

Which is richt enough, if ye think aboot it. They spend thoosans advertisin that ye shouldna let strangers in yer hoose athoot askin for identification first, bit they nivver tell ye fit the identification looks like so ye can identify them. Bliddy queer, that.

Onywye, he seemed a genuine kinna blokie. "Hiv ye ony problems wi yer hoose?" he says. Well, it so happened I did hae a problem. It wis lucky he came roon.

A twa-three wikks afore, I'd been affa bothered wi dandruff. I went til the chemist and a' thing. "Hiv ye onything for dandruff?" I says, and this little slip o' a quinie telt me I "must eat only pure foods and stop smoking" because I wis pollutin ma body and it wis rebellin by giein me a bad dose o' dandruff. Then she gave me a bottlie o' yalla stuff for massagin intil ma scalp. What affa-smellin stuff. Cats wis followin me aboot for days.

Well, I persevered wi that stuff, bit it didna hae ony effect. Ma jacket wis aye covered in dandruff. Waur nor ivver. So I went back til the chemist and I says: "Lassie, yer lotion's nae worth a docken. Maybe I'm nae workin it richt. Wid ye come roon by the nicht and show me yer massagin technique?"

She widna hear o't, of coorse. Silly lassie. She askit if I wis aff the fags and eatin only pure foods and I said I wis. So she hands me this bottle o' blue stuff and bids me try it for anither wikk. Well, I tried it. It didna mak nae odds, bit I tried it. And ma dandruff jist got worse. I wis covered in the stuff.

"Lassie," I says on ma next visit, "that's affa stuff ye're giein me. Ye'd better hurry wi a cure or I'll hae nae heid left."

It wis green stuff next time.

It didna work, eether.

And that wis fan I discovered it wisna dandruff. It wis ma livin-room ceilin that wis flakin.

So fan the blokie came roon I showed him the ceilin and he says: "Evidently, you have been smoking too much, Mr Sotter. It has affected the life-expectancy of the paint covering adversely. I will arrange to have it painted for you, but I must ask you to desist from smoking in the house if we are to prevent a recurrence."

"Fairly that, captain," I says. "I'm aff the fags noo, onywye. And I'm eatin only pure foods." Funny how ye get intil the set o' something, isn't it?

So I got the ceilin sortit oot and, ach, the smell o' pent wis drivin me up the wa. It's an affa sickly smell, isn't it? So I thocht, well, I'll phone ma son and his wife at Portsoy and see if I can bide wi them a coupla days. They said I wis welcome ony time.

So I went up til Portsoy and I spent a coupla days wanderin aboot. A bonnie placie, Portsoy. Pearl o' the Banffshire Coast. I went roon the herber. I saw far the aul station wis. And I sat on a bench wi a coupla locals and newsed wi them.

And then I took a notion for an ice-cream, and I ken they've affa fine ice-cream at Portsoy. So I went intil the shoppie, and I said: "I'll tak a slider, ma dear. Bit only if yer ice-cream is absolutely pure."

She says: "Sir," she says. "This ice-cream is as pure as the girl o' yer dreams."

I says: "In that case, jist gie's a packet o' fags."

FLO SPURTLE

Full name: Florence Spurtle
Age: 32
Marital Status: Married
Lives: With husband, Gibby, son, Wayne, and daughter, Cassandra
House: Two-bedroom semi in middle of village

IF ANY o' you ladies are married, ye'll ken the sort o' trouble I've endured this past year. They're like little laddies, men, aren't they? It's nae wives they need; it's skivvies and nannies. If ye're nae rinnin at their heels, ye're leadin them by the nose. I'm fed up o't.

I blew ma stack in May. It wisna really fair on Gibby. It jist came oot o' the blue and I exploadit at him. You ladies'll understand. Things jist build up inside ye and ye maun let them oot, and usually it's somebody completely innocent that bears the brunt o't.

I'd come back fae the shop wi ma messages and I walked in the back door. There he wis, fixin next door's motorbike on the kitchen table and he hidna put doon a newspaper or nithing. Great big pipes and gears and ither iley things on my new seersucker cloth.

I handed him ma message-bag.

"That's yer goin-away present," I said.

"Am I gaun awa?" he said.

"I bliddy hope so," I said. "Or I'll be up in coort the morn for murder."

Ye ken this? Even efter half an oor shoutin and bawlin and hittin him, he still couldna see fit wis wrang. That's jist my Gibby, of coorse. He's nae the sharpest loon, bit he's a fine loon. Fin he's sleepin.

Yet there's times I feel sorry for him, really. He's nae a bad lad. He's gweed-hertit. He's a good faither til Wayne and Cassandra. And it canna hae been easy, bein unemployed a' that time. I lost coont o' a' the jobs he tried for and didna get. And a' the jobs he did get and got the sack fae. It depresses ye efter a while, realisin ye're mairried til a neep.

Bit a neep wi feelins.

I mind back in February, we wis jist sittin at teatime, watchin Tak the High Road, and he wis slumped in the easy cheir, nae sayin much o' nithing then, at half-time, he looks at me and he says: "Flo," he says. "I think I'm hamesick."

I lookit at him for a twa-three seconds, then I crossed and I sat on the airm o' the cheir and I took his hand and I clappit it and I said: "Hamesick, Gibby? Hamesick? How can ye be hamesick? This *is* yer hame."

"I ken," he said. "And I'm sick o't."

Ye see fit I mean? He's got his feelins, even though he maybe looks lik a great big bruiser. He's quite sensitive, really.

Gibby's big problem is that he still taks a bucket. Now that he's got a job at Crochlie Neuk as their gairdner, he's got a bittie mair siller in his pooch. Twa-three nichts a wikk, he'll be doon at the pubbie.

I dinna grudge him a nicht oot, for it must get really borin, a man o' his age stuck in a little villagie lik this. If only he wisna so generous wi his money. A'b'dy taps him for cash. I believe his nickname's Clydesdale. I aye thocht it wis because he wis built lik a real worker. It's nae. It's because he's aye good for a fiver.

Then they jist egg him on and he dis daft things.

It's affection he's needin, really. I saw that on TV. Men that caper aboot were brocht up by affa difficult mothers, so they caper aboot for attention and affection. And they end up deein daft things and they canna see that folk are lachin *at* them, nae *wi* them.

Erchie Sotter took him hame the ither nicht and he said that Gibby wis feelin a bittie sick. I've nivver seen Gibby lookin that green. He wis groanin and a' thing. It turned oot he'd tried drinkin a goldfish bowl. I ask ye, a *goldfish* bowl.

He'd been a wee bittie drunk and his so-called pals had telt him the goldfish bowl wis a big gin-and-tonic. Fa needs pals like that?

So he'd drunk nearly the hale lot until he twigged something wis wrang. He only stopped because he windered why the slice o' lemon kept jumpin oot o' his moo.

GIBBY SPURTLE

Full name: Gilbert Albert Spurtle
Age: 34
Marital Status: Married
Lives: With wife, Flo, son, Wayne, and daughter, Cassandra
House: Two-bedroom semi in middle of village

FA wid be a parent? They said it wid be a big responsibility, bit they nivver tell ye how much o' a responsibility it'll really be. It fears me sometimes. I'm in ma thirties and I still dinna feel able copin wi twa kids o' ma ain.

It's a thocht, isn't it? Twa little folk dependin on ye for a'thing. Their hale futures shapit by you. It's worryin really. And I look at Wayne and I think: "Far did we go wrang?"

It's nae that he's a coorse loon. His hert's in the richt place. He's jist ill-trickit, really. A bit o' a nickum. I wis the same at his age. He's jist got an affa reputation in the village for impidence and mischief. And he winna tak a tellin.

The worst o' bein a parent, accordin til Walter Dreep, is fan they start askin questions aboot the Birds and the Bees. I've been dreadin that day almost since the loon wis born. I tak a reid face affa easy. I widna ken fit ti say. It's nae easy, is it? Ye kinna hope they'll jist pick things up, or they'll learn it at the school. Bit ye're nivver really sure.

I saw this article in one o' Flo's magazines and it said the danger time wis fan a new baby came intil the femly because the first child wid start askin a' the difficult questions. Far did the baby come fae? How did it get up there? Will it be goin back if we dinna like it? Could we nae get a puppy instead? Stuff like that.

Fan we knew Flo wis expectin again wi Cassandra, I reminded her aboot that story in the magazine and she said that if we made a fuss o' Wayne and remindit him that he wis still important, there widna be ony problem.

And, sure enough, he nivver said onything — til the day Flo took Cassandra hame fae the hospital. She walkit up the path wi Cassandra cooried doon in this great big tartan travellin-rug.

Wayne wis playin wi his toys aside the fireplace and Flo jist came in and laid this bundle doon on the sofa and she said: "Here ye go, Wayne. This is fit ye've been waitin for."

Ye ken fit he said?

He said: "Is it an Action Man?"

Well, we jist lached. "No," I said. "It's nae an Action Man."

"A new fitba?"

"No, nae that, eether."

Then he thocht a bittie harder for a coupla seconds and he said: "It's nae a Thunderbird, is it?"

"No," said Flo. "It's yer new baby sister. Awa and tak a lookie."

And we watched him as he liftit himsel up fae his toys at the fireside and he trottit across til the travellin-rug. He looked back at us and we nodded at him and he bent doon, real gentle-like, and he opened up this little parcellie o' humanity.

And ye ken fit he said?

He said: "Ooooooh." That wis a' he said. Jist: "Ooooooh." Really lovin-like. As if he wis jist captured wi the magic o' it a'.

"Isn't she bonnie, Wayne?" I said.

"She hisna ony teeth," he said. And we jist smiled. "And she hisna ony hair. And she hisna got a nose. Or eyes. Or lugs. Jist a great big wide smile."

Well, of coorse, he'd opened the wrang end o' the travellin-rug.

It's been plain sailin ever since that first day.

Well, nearly plain-sailin. He did ask a coupla questions aboot the Birds and the Bees, bit nae nithing Flo couldna cope wi at the time. He asked far Cassandra had come fae and Flo telt him. Real matter o' fact like.

There were whiles he got a bittie jealous, though. I mind one day I came in and I found him diggin aneth the gooseberry bushes at the fit o' the gairden.

"Wayne," I said. "Ye're nae diggin for anither baby sister, are ye? Ye ken fine that babies dinna come fae under gooseberry bushes."

"I'm nae lookin for a new sister," he said.

"I'm pittin this een back."

WAYNE SPURTLE

Full name: Wayne Jason Dominic Spurtle
Age: 9
Marital Status: Single
Lives: With father, Gibby, mother, Flo, and sister, Cassandra
House: Two-bedroom semi in middle of village

IT'S BEEN a worryin year for oor femly. Back in April, ma mither wis greetin. She said we'd been gettin threatenin letters. I said I wid rin til the police station, bit she said it widna dee ony good. The letters wis fae the Income Tax.

I'm only nine. I'm jist tellin ye that because I dinna undertand why parents canna leave little kids ti be little kids. One o' my first memories is me throwin a tantrum in a big shop in Aiberdeen because ma mither widna buy me an ice-cream. I must hiv been three or four. And she said: "For goodness sake, Wayne! Act yer age!"

Ye see fit I mean? Fan ye're little, they wish ye were bigger. Fan ye're bigger, they wish ye were bigger still. And fan ye're reeeeally big, they wish ye were little again. I've seen it happenin wi ma cousins. Funny folk, mams and dads.

And Dad's aye askin aboot fit I wint ti be. I said I wid like ti be a minister. They only work one day a wikk and they get a free hoose. He kent I wisna bein serious.

"No," he said. "Fit kinna career wid ye like? Go on, tell me."

I said: "Dad, I'm only nine. I dinna ken."

He said: "Nine's a big loon. Ye should be thinkin o' yer future. I didna think o' my future and look fit happened til me."

So I startit thinkin aboot ma future that very day. And ye ken this? I still dinna ken fit I wid like ti be. I'd like a job that involves a lotta travel. Big money. Big cars. A Nintendo. And plenty sweeties. Ony ideas?

They tried a test on me nae lang ago. I ken fine. They thocht it wis a secret, bit I wis listenin at their bedroom door fan they planned it.

Dad put a £10 note doon on the livin-room table. Next til that, he put a Bible. Aside that, he put a bottle o' whisky.

He'd read it in some magazine that ye can usually tell fit a kid'll be by the sorta things he's interestit in at eight or nine. Dad thocht the money wid show I wis keen on big business. He thocht the Bible wid be the Kirk. And he thocht the whisky wid be an idle layaboot.

Then they hid in the big press aside the china cabinet and waitit. So I went intil the livin-room and played aboot for a few minutes makkin on I hidna noticed the

three things lyin on the table. Then I saw them. I looked roon aboot as if I wis checkin that I wis really masel. Then I pickit up the £10 note and I lookit at it, and I heard ma mither whisperin: "He'll be a businessman! He'll be a businessman! We'll retire and he'll keep's in the lappa luxury!"

Then I put doon the money and I pickit up the Bible. I flickit through the Bible and studied it for a few minties and then I heard her sayin: "It's the Bible. It's the Bible. He'll be a minister. What proud we'll be."

So I put doon the Bible and I pickit up the bottle o' whisky. I heard her groanin and sayin: "He'll be a waster. He'll be a waster. I'll be black-affrontit. Twa in the same femly."

So I put the whisky bottle doon on the table again. Then I made on I wis studyin a' three things at the same time. I could hear them affa excitit in the press. Parents must think kids are saft.

I walkit roon aboot the table twa-three times. Then I touched the £10 note. There wis this excitit squeal fae the press. "A businessman! A businessman!"

Then I touched the Bible.

"A minister! A minister!"

Then I touched the bottle o' whisky.

"Oh me! A waster!"

Then I pickit up the money *and* the Bible *and* the whisky and walkit towards the door.

And I heard ma dad say:

"Oh my God. A cooncillor!"

Rev MONTGOMERY THOLE

Full name: The Rev. Montgomery Matthew Lazarus Thole BD
Age: 40
Marital Status: Married
Lives: With wife and mother
House: Four-bedroom granite manse at end of village

HELLO! And may I say what a pleasure it is to be able to spend these few minutes in your company. I'm the minister. Montgomery Thole. You can call me Montgomery. And I hope we'll be seeing a lot more of you in the coming months.

How has my year been at Stronach? Well, as you know, I'm not indigent, which is to say that I can't claim to have been born and bred in the village, but fresh blood is so important, don't you think? And the villagers have been very understanding. They have tried so hard to make me feel part of their small community. For my part, I have tried to minister to them empathetically and sympathetically.

When I conducted my first funeral, the village seemed very impressed. At the tea afterwards, they came up to me one by one and said they hadn't known a service quite like it. One gentleman said that at one point he thought it might as well have been a memorial for a sack of tatties. What a *marvellous* compliment; potatoes being one of the essentials of life; the very spirit of rural existence. I was quietly chuffed when I heard that. Approbation is so important, don't you agree?

Of course, things haven't always been so cosy. Not at all. When first I arrived at the end of 1990, I knew that I had to make my mark very quickly. The Kirk Session had told me that and, frankly, my old professor at university had always suggested that a little fire and brimstone in the early days of a new charge helps waken a soporific congregation.

I had been wondering what theme to take as my first sermon when my wife and my mother, carousing after an evening at choir practice and flinging wide all the doors of the kitchen cabinets in their quest for a sweet sherry, provided me with the answer.

The demon drink.

I spent two nights writing that sermon. It was so important to me that it went down well. That sermon was to be more than just 15 minutes in the pulpit. It was to convey my very image and principle to the people to whom I had come to minister. It would anchor me in their minds for the rest of my tenure.

Anyway, though I say so myself, I was rather chuffed with it. I was. Definitely a fire-and-brimstone piece. My old prof would have been proud.

I took as my text Luke 21, v34-36. "Who is the richest man in town?" I thundered. "It is the innkeeper! The keeper of the public house!"

They were quite mesmerised. I don't think they had been used to *tours de force*. "Who has the biggest car? The keeper of the public house!

"Who has the finest clothes? The best food? The grandest home? Why, the keeper of the public house!"

And then I paused for a moment for effect, which is a little trick I learned in my student days. And I said in quite a low voice:

"And who is responsible? My friends, it is you. You! You are the people who provide this man with his finery and riches. You are the people who spend your hard-earned money in a den of alcohol and drinking and iniquity and allow the saloon-keeper to live in such lavishness and riches."

There was a silence, and then a small excited buzz ran round the church. I can't tell you what a thrill it is for a clergyman to have such an effect on a congregation. I was ... chuffed. Absolutely chuffed.

Oh, I don't doubt that there were some who took offence. I don't doubt that there were some who "didst murmur against the good man of the house" (Matt. 20, v11). But you can't make an omelette without breaking eggs, I always say.

Alas, pride cometh before a fall. Over the course of the following week, I inquired of people in the street if they had approved of my sermon, even although it had preached against the evils of alcohol. Had all this talk of ill-spent money and obscene riches changed their lives?

"Michty, aye, meenister," they said. "We're thinkin o' buyin a pub."

The
Stories

A meal for two

Episode 88 : July 1, 1989

LIFE was being uncommon kind to Gibby Spurtle: expecting a happy event in six weeks and now an entrepreneur of some reputation thanks to his fruit stall in the centre of the village. Although not overburdened with grey matter, Gibby feels his ship has come in at last and, as any true entrepreneur would, has decided to push the boat out.

At least, so Flo, his heavily pregnant wife, revealed during her latest home-help stint at Babbie Girn's.

"He's takkin's oot for a celebration meal," she confessed, daydreaming over a sinkful of dishes. "My Gibby's richt romantic fan the occasion needs."

Babbie sat in her easy chair, scowling darkly, for it was Babbie's home-baking enterprise which had been ruined by Gibby's unexpected success at selling bashed fruit.

"Aye," said Flo. "He's sparin nae expinse. Siller nae objeck. A richt slap-up feed." She busied herself anew with a dirty saucepan. After a few good skirps round the sides with a mop on a stick, she spoke again.

"He's promised that he winna show's up, eether," she said. "Well, he's nae that acquant wi funcy aetin, bit he says he'll fairly mak an effort. He's got a new sark. He's pressin his ganzie. He's cleanin aneth his fingernails and a'thing."

"Love's a marvellous thing, richt enough," muttered Babbie in the living-room.

Flo attacked a casserole with renewed vigour, set it up on the draining-board, and spoke again.

"He's nae a bad aul stick, really," she said. "We hae wir ups and doons. We bawl and shout. He hits me and I batter him ... ye ken, the normal femly things ... bit fan ye stan back and tak a richt good look at him ... Lord, he's a fine-set figure o' a man."

"He's got a face I'd nivver tire o' kickin," muttered Babbie.

"Fit's that?" said Flo, who had strolled through to the living-room and was now standing behind Babbie.

"I said he's jist a romantic nickum," said Babbie hastily.

"I ken," sighed Flo.

THE slap-up romantic meal turned out to be a supper at the Stronach Arms. Since Flo is a part-time waitress at the Stronach Arms and knows what foul calumnies are perpetrated in the kitchen, Gibby's choice might have been better.

However, not even that seemed to dampen her spirits as Gibby ushered her to her table. He arranged himself prominently at one side while Flo hoisted herself and the prominent bump that was her tummy and flopped into the other chair.

Gibby looked around and nodded and smiled at what few other guests there

were — mostly tourists — and fancied they knew they were in the presence of an incipient business genius.

The hotel-owner came by and was surprised to see one of his junior staff toffed up to the nines and sitting at one of the dining-room's best tables (the one next to the juke box and just to the left of the TV).

"Mr and Mrs Spurtle," he said, veiling the surprise only thinly. "Celebration is it? What can I get you?"

Gibby looked at Flo and shot a very deliberate wink in her direction. "We will tak a gander at yer ally cart menu, if you please. Chop-chop," he said, and he winked again at Flo, acknowledging that he was playing his role as bon-viveur and boule-vardier to the hilt and that he was certainly not affronting her.

Presently, the owner returned with two menus and the wine list. He was about to hand Gibby the wine list when he stopped.

"If I may say so, Mr Spurtle," he said, "this being a celebration, I think you should celebrate with a very special wine."

Gibby smiled and shot a quick glance at his wallet. " Fairly that," he said, his suave assurance crumbling slightly.

The owner smiled and leaned closer to Gibby, as if to add to the air of mystery for Flo. "Down in the cellar," he said, "we have a vintage bottle that should just suit you."

"Na, na, na," said Gibby. "We're nae sikkin neen o' yer mochey aul dirt. We'll tak a new bottle aff yer sideboord."

Ye dinna play aboot wi choobs

Episode 89 : July 8, 1989

PULLING her collar up around her neck and sporting the darkest of dark glasses, Kate Barrington-Graham scuttled from her Volvo estate car and into the Stronach Health Centre. She closed the door behind her; peered between the venetian-blind slats to be sure no one had noticed her, and tiptoed across to the receptionist.

"Mrs Barrington-Graham," she whispered. "Eight-thirty appointment." The receptionist did not look up, for Mrs Barrington-Graham had whispered so softly that the receptionist had not heard.

She cleared her throat. "Mrs Katherine Barrington-Graham," she said. "I had an eight-thirty appointment."

"And now it's ten-fifteen," said the receptionist, still checking off figures on a computer screen in front of her.

"Yes, indeed," said Mrs Barrington-Graham. "I'm a trifle late, I know, but it's such a dreadful kerfuffle getting the domestic help sorted out with her chores every morning. Why I employ the woman I really haven't the faintest. And my husband, Godfrey — he's in practice in Aberdeen, you know — well, his Mercedes was running a little roughly this morning. Unusual for a Mercedes, don't you think? And, well, it all took time to sort out. Life's such a *trial*."

"The waiting-room is over there," said the receptionist, pointing to the corner, but still not looking up. Mrs Barrington-Graham walked across, stumbled down the step because she was still wearing the sunglasses and hastily closed the door behind her.

"Doctor," said the receptionist on her intercom, "that's your eight-thirty; that dreadful, pompous old besom who can't bear to be seen using the NHS."

"Thank you, Janice," said the doctor. "We'll leave her stewing for a wee whilie and I'll finish off a few things in here, I think."

MRS Barrington-Graham glanced round the waiting-room and sighed with relief when she saw no one else was in. She removed her dark glasses; turned down the collar of her Burberry, and picked a seat as far from the window as possible.

After a few moments' introspection, she began sifting idly through the magazines. Bimbo, Twinkle, BoBo Bunny. Not a Harpers & Queen in sight. She moved on to the next rack of magazines. Pippin, Rag Tag and Bobtail, Health and Efficiency.

"My goodness," she thought. "That disgusting lecher Mr Sotter has been here," and she drew her coat round about her and decided instead to gaze at the wallposters.

Just then, the myopic face of Mrs Dorothy Birze appeared, scowling behind jam-jar-thick spectacles as she tried to make out the blurry shapes before her.

DOCTOR

"Hullo," she shouted. "Fa's that? Is that you?"

Kate Barrington-Graham did not reply, lest Mrs Birze sat down beside her which, of course, was exactly what Dorothy did.

"I'm richt pleased there's some ither body here," said Dorothy, boring her face almost into the side of Mrs Barrington-Graham's neck. "I aye thinks waitin-rooms is richt caul, clinical kinna places."

"It is a clinic, after all," sniffed Mrs Barrington-Graham.

"Mrs Barrington-Graham," said Dorothy, having recognised the voice. "We hinna met afore, bit I'd ken yer voice onywye. It wid scrape sharn aff a spad. Fit's worst wi ye?"

"I beg your pardon," said Mrs Barrington-Graham. "I prefer not to discuss the intimacies of my medication with a complete stranger." She harumphed; pulled a corner of her coat from beneath Dorothy's behind and stared fixedly at the wall.

"Dorothy Birze is my name," said Dorothy. "You can ca me Dosh. Now, that's us introduced formal-like. Fit's worst wi ye?"

Mrs Barrington-Graham glowered a pointed glower but, of course, this was lost entirely on someone as myopic as Dorothy, who sat expectantly, bearing an empty, cheesy grin and blinking occasionally.

"I prefer not to say, thank you," said Mrs Barrington-Graham.

"Is't yer choobs?" asked Dorothy. "I hope it's nae yer choobs. Choobs is nae for playin aboot wi at your age. I've aye said: 'Lord, I dinna mind broken legs, sair jints or hirply feet, bit spare me ma choobs.' "

"My 'tubes' are in perfect running order, thank you for asking," said Mrs Barrington-Graham.

"Are ye sure, though?" said Dorothy, leaning closer. "Ye look lik a richt choob case ti me. As seen's I clappit een on ye, I says: 'Aye,' I says, 'that's choobs and nae mistake.' Ye've got choobs wrote a' ower ye."

Mrs Barrington-Graham stayed silent, evidently hoping to freeze out Dorothy, but she had not bargained on Dorothy's innate North-east tenacity.

"I come originally fae Methlick masel," she said. "We'd a puckle richt good choob cases ower there. The doctors at For'sterhill were aye sayin: 'Aye, Methlick's a rare place for choobs. Choobs ower the heid at Methlick.' "

Mrs Barrington-Graham picked up a 1979 copy of Bimbo, evidently hoping Dorothy would take the hint but, of course, when you can't see someone is fed up with you, you rattle on regardless.

"There wis this ae wifie," said Dorothy. "She lookit jist lik you're lookin ivnoo — washed-oot lookin. Well, this wifie wis taen intil For'sterhill; amb'lance rippin ben the roads lik I dinna ken fit."

Kate Barrington-Graham turned and looked at Dorothy, for Dorothy was getting thoroughly caught up in the drama of the tale.

"Aye," said Dorothy, lowering her voice for dramatic effect. "Jinkin roon corners. Blue licht flashin. Police escort. Through traffic lichts athoot stoppin. This wye. That wye. Up and doon. Passin cars. Passin larries. Passin buses. Passin a'thing. What a lick they were at wi themsels. I dinna ken how they didna hae a smash, they were in sic a hurry."

Mrs Barrington-Graham could not help but be mesmerised by such a graphic tale, so well told, and she found herself listening intently while trying to look uninterested at the same time.

"Well," said Dorothy, almost breathless herself. "This wifie wis raced intil the operatin theeter and thon surgeons wis intil her intimmers lik a knife through marg. Well, they wheepit oot this and they wheepit oot that. Wheep, wheep, wheep. They wheepit oot that much that I sweir there must hiv been aboot nithing left."

Then Dorothy paused for dramatic effect, and sat back in her chair, leaving Mrs Barrington-Graham high and dry.

Mrs Barrington-Graham looked at her.

"And?" she said primly.

"Eh?" said Dorothy.

"So what happened next?" said Mrs Barrington-Graham.

"Oh, then they shooed her up again and wheeled her up til a side ward." Dorothy paused for a moment, glowing with the excitement of a tale well told.

Mrs Barrington-Graham waited for the punchline, but none came. After a respectful silence, she felt obliged to press for an end to the story.

"And now she's healthy, fit and up and about again, I suppose?" she inquired in as offhand a manner as she could muster lest she betray her interest.

"Eh?" said Dorothy.

"I say she'll be up and about again as fit as a fiddle," said Mrs Barrington-Graham.

"Fiddle?" scoffed Dorothy. "Fit as a fiddle? Awa ye go. She turned up her taes jist ten minutes efter she wis put intil the ward. Poppit her clogs. Up the golden staircase. Snuffed it.

"That's fit I'm tellin ye.

"Ye dinna play aboot wi choobs."

Babbie's bout of late-life crisis

Episode 91 : July 22, 1989

IT WAS a normal Saturday morning at Stronach Emporium and General Stores, with villagers queuing patiently for their shopping and enjoying time for a news, while Ebenezer Grip stepped back and forth behind the old wooden counter, reaching up to high shelves for packets of this and bending down to low shelves for tinnies of that.

At least, it *was* quiet until the door opened and in rushed Flo Spurtle, scanning the faces in the queue until she spotted Virginia Huffie, second from the front. Virginia looked back to see who had just come in. At the moment they saw each other, Virginia realised something was wrong and stepped out of the queue. The two women left the shop and a buzz of excited conversation began as soon as they had left.

"Michty, Flo," said Virginia as soon as they were outside. "There's something wrang, lassie. I can see that."

"It's Mrs Girn," puffed Flo. "I'm affa worried aboot her. She's nae hersel. Nae hersel ata. I left her hoose efter ma home-help stint this mornin and there's something far wrang."

"Such as?" said Virginia.

"I winna beat aboot the bush, Virginia," said Flo. "In my opinion, she micht be thinkin o' suicide."

Virginia burst out laughing. "Michty, Flo," she said. "Jist because Babbie barks at ye and roars and says she'd be better aff deid disna mean she'll kill hersel. That's jist Babbie's wye. I've kent her near sivventy year and she's aye been the same. Dinna think nithing o' that."

"That's jist it," said Flo. "I ken Babbie fine. The hale problem is that she's *nae* barkin and roarin. She's hardly sayin onything. She's nae even bothered dressin hersel yet. She's affa doon aboot the mou."

Virginia stopped. Flo stopped, too. "Maybe I will tak a lookie in on her," said Virginia.

VIRGINIA didn't bother knocking at Babbie's front door but marched straight into the living-room to find Babbie, in her housecoat, staring aimlessly into the empty grate. "Are ye a'richt?" asked Virginia, walking over to the easy chair and clapping Babbie's hand gently.

"As weel's can be expeckit in the circumstances," said Babbie, still not looking up. "As weel as can be expeckit for an aul hen lik me. For an aul, hallyrackit hen."

"Oh, my," said Virginia sitting down in the other easy chair at the opposite side of the fireplace. "This is nae the Babbie Girn I ken ava. This sounds lik someb'dy feelin sorry for hersel."

"Is that so?" said Babbie. "Well, well, well. Feelin sorry for masel. And hiv I nae reason for feelin sorry for masel? Eh? I'm near sivventy. On the pinsion. Nae close femly. Bide masel. Nithing ti look forrit til bit Tak the High Road. Fit hiv I ti be cheery aboot?"

Babbie looked up with heavy eyes. "I've lost ma youth, Virginia. I've turned aul afore ma time. I've lost ma figure. I've lost ma looks. I'm an aul wifie and I nivver even noticed it happenin."

Virginia paused for a moment, puzzled at the concept that Babbie had somewhere lost her looks. "Ye're needin a good day oot, that's fit you're needin," she said. "I see the Alford Cavalcade's on the day. Fit aboot a tekkie ower there?"

Babbie sighed again. "Nuh," she said. "I ken they're toppers o' folk at Alford, bit I canna be deein wi aul cars. They jist remind me that they're aul crocks and

54

they're the same age as me." She turned and stared into the ashes in the grate again.

"Right," said Virginia, taking charge. "Nae mair o' this mopin. There's a bussie intil the toon in half an oor. We're gaun in for a rake and a new rigoot til ye. Cheer ye up. There's nithing lik a new frock ti lift yer spirits. Awa and get yersel riggit."

SATURDAY morning is a busy time in Aberdeen and Babbie was not really in the mood for crowds. They trekked from dress shop to dress shop until they came upon one in a small back lane with stock suited to the more mature, more-upholstered lady. Virginia and Babbie looked at the window display and then Virginia dragged Babbie inside. The noise and bustle of the city faded behind them as Virginia closed the door.

The somewhat aloof-looking shop assistant ambled across. "Yes?" she said.

"We wis winderin if ye've a frockie ti fit ma friend here," said Virginia sweetly.

The woman turned away to the stockroom muttering (Virginia could have sworn): "If I have, I'm sacking the buyer."

Presently, she returned with a selection of three, all extremely colourful. By sheer good fortune, the first one Babbie tried fitted and suited her to a T. She couldn't have found a better-fitting, more flattering garment than if it had been made especially for her. And the transformation couldn't have been more amazing. Virginia watched as a reluctant smile spread across Babbie's chiselled features. Babbie looked at herself in the full-length mirror. The navy blue of the dress picked out the silvery highlights in her hairnet, and the ochre contrasted well with the broken veins in her nose.

The assistant and Virginia were genuinely pleased. "That really suits ye, Babbie," said Virginia. Babbie was still turning this way and that in front of the mirror. "And it's only thirty-two poun, tee," said Virginia. "I'll chip in and we'll ca it yer birthday."

Babbie was definitely perking up. The more she looked at herself, the broader her smile grew. "Dis it really suit me?" she said. "Ye're nae jist sayin it? Dis it really mak a difference?"

"It makes madam look ten years younger," said the shop assistant truthfully. "If I might suggest, a toning pair of stockings would just set you off. If you don't mind my saying, the pair you have are getting a bit saggy and baggy round the ankles."

Instantly, Babbie's face changed. "That's it," she snapped. "Tak yer frock and stuff it." She stamped off to the changing-room, changed in less than two minutes and stormed out of the shop, trailing a dumbfounded Virginia in her wake.

"That wis a bittie excessive, Babbie," said Virginia, when she felt the heat of the moment had died down. "She jist suggestit a new paira stockins."

"Nithing o' the kind excessive," snapped Babbie, still marching huffily towards the bus station. "Saggy and baggy roon the unkles?

"I'm nae *weerin* nae stockins."

Walter wants a jube-jube

Episode 92 : July 29, 1989

AFTER six months of hottering on the edge of expiry, Walter Dreep's father, Dode, sighed his last and so another Stronacher went to meet his maker. His widow was chillingly composed at the funeral and insisted on going to the graveside. Folk in the village said it was the mark of the woman. "A hard-faced een, that," observed Babbie Girn at the cemetery gates. "Hard as they come."

Everyone knew what Babbie meant, for Mother Dreep is known throughout the howe for a severity which eclipses even Babbie's: at least Babbie has a dry humour about her.

At 92, Mother Dreep rules what is left of the Dreep clan in iron manner. Folk say that Walter is as wet as his mother is domineering. Mother Dreep still pops a jube-jube into her son's mouth when he visits. "Walter!" she'll cry. "Ma handbag!" And Walter knows it's jube-jube time so he scuttles off for his mother's portmanteau. Walter's wife, Aggie, seethes quietly, for she and Mother Dreep have never hit it off. Two wilful women rarely do.

After the funeral, Mother Dreep held court at a buffet at the Stronach Arms; her granite features surveying the assembled company from a tall chair brought in specially at her demand. As friends munched their way through chopped-pork sandwiches, sausage rolls and rock cakes, Mother Dreep received each one in turn.

"Aye," she growled at Erchie Sotter, "he's better aff awa fae't a'. I'll be honest; it's a relief. He turned affa sookit-lookin at the hinder end. Nae himsel ava. He's nae sufferin nae mair." And Erchie nodded sagely and passed on in his quest for a good malt.

"How hiv ye been keepin, Mrs Dreep?" inquired Virginia Huffie gently. "I wyte it's been a tryin time for ye this last six month."

"It his that, Miss Huffie," said Mother Dreep, hysting her bosom underneath her big, black, pre-war coat which smelled of mothballs. "I've nae hid a winka sleep for wikks. Wi the strain o't a', I've nae been … ye ken … regular, doon below. It's been a sair tyauve and I'm nae affrontit til admit it. No."

Virginia flushed at Mother Dreep's intimate alimentary details and stood back with an embarrassed half-smile on her face.

"I wis that sorry for yer loss," said Dorothy Birze, moving in and clapping Mother Dreep's hand softly. "I didna ken him masel, but I could aye hear him lachin lik a drain in his sickbed ilky nicht I was oot walkin the dog."

"Well, he's nae lachin noo," said Mother Dreep. "Ye're richt, though. Lord, he wis aye lachin. Aye lachin. Couldna stop him if he got startit. He could walk intil a room lachin; bide there for half-an-oor lachin, and leave again, still lachin. A'body crowdit roon aboot him. Ye nivver saw him doon aboot the mou. He'd aye a great big cheesy grin on his face."

Mother Dreep fell silent and, for a moment, Dorothy felt awkward. "Aye," said Mother Dreep, "a richt gype, and nae mistak."

Then Walter cruised past, a tray of sandwiches in his hand. Mother Dreep spotted him and broke off her conversation with Dorothy. "Walter!" she called. "Ma handbag!" And Walter toddled off.

To save embarrassment in front of Stronach, he moved to a dark corner, fumbled in his mother's handbag for the jube-jube packet and popped a small pastille in his mouth. He walked back to the centre of the room and handed over the bag. "It's a'richt, mother," he whispered. "I've taen ma jube-jube already." And he smiled and showed it clenched between his dentures.

"That's jist typical o' you, Walter," said Mother Dreep. "Typical. Ye're selfish enough ti think I'd worry aboot you and yer dampt jube-jube at a time lik this. Ma man nae caul in his grave yet?" She glowered at her son, whose shoulders began sagging. "Na," she said, opening the bag. "It's a fag I'm wintin." And she rummled about inside her trusty portmanteau, her feeble eyes peering into the depths.

"Onywye," she said as she fumbled. "I've nae jube-jubes the day. I've jist ma fags, ma spunks and this ..." And she held up a small plastic bag.

"Fit's that?" said Walter.

"The chemist came roon by wi them yestreen," said Mother Dreep.

"Glycerine suppositories."

Waiting for the New Year sale

Episode 114 : December 30, 1989

THE concept of the New Year sale has come late to Stronach. As with other modern shopping ploys, such as self-service and home delivery, New Year sales have yet to sully the commerce of the village. Increasingly, though, shopkeeper Ebenezer Grip has become throughly disenchanted with the amount of trade being spirited off to stores in Aberdeen by New Year sales there. So this year he has felt forced to join them (because he can't beat them). Come Wednesday, the SALE stickers had been printed up, delivered and put in position in the shop windows.

When Babbie Girn was picking up her weekly quarter-pound of pottit heid, she inquired about the stickers. "Aye, weel," said Ebenezer cagily. "It's an experiment. It disna start till Setterday. If it disna go doon weel, it winna be repeatit."

"Oh," said Babbie. "Ye mean if the customers dinna like yer sale, ye winna hae anither een?"

"No," said Ebenezer. "If *I* dinna like the sale, I winna hae anither een."

And so all the notables of Stronach womanhood came to be standing patiently outside the Emporium on Saturday morning, message-bags in the crooks of their arms.

Ebenezer, meanwhile, had deliberately delayed the opening of the store, presumably in a vain attempt at showmanship and the creation of pre-sale tension and atmosphere. So while people such as Babbie Girn, Dorothy Birze, Virginia Huffie, Aggie Dreep, Claire Macfarlane and Geneva Brose stood and waited, they discussed how their Christmas had gone.

Eventually, as it became clear that Ebenezer intended to build up more of an atmosphere than even Stronach expected, they were forced along less familiar avenues of conversation.

"Lord, it's been a richt kirn-up at the end o' the year, hisn't it?" said Aggie. "Ilky day ye open yer paper, there's a new steer-up somewye."

"I ken," said Virginia. "First the Iron Curtain comes doon lik a packa cards. Then Muggie's hauled ower the coals for a' yon Boat People. And noo it's ower in Romania far it's a' happenin."

There was a mild buzz of agreement in the ranks as everyone nodded sagely and shuffled their feet.

"That Romanian boy, Cockachesscoo," said Geneva. "He didna hae a very happy Christmas, did he? Ae minute, he wis sittin there, mindin his ain business, sitting doon til his Christmas turkey. The next, up in front o' the firin squad. BANG! Nae even time for his trifle."

There was another mild buzz of agreement round the group.

"Aye," said Babbie. "A firin squad fair pits a dumper on yer Christmas. It must hiv been a richt flat festive season amon the Cockachesscoo femly efter that."

"Oh, bit what affa things he did," cautioned Virginia. "Did ye nae see the news? Did ye nae read the papers? He wis waur nor Hitler, wis Cockachesscoo. Murderin, torturin, saltin awa great piles o' ither folk's siller ... fit a' did he nae dee?"

"Starvin the Romanians," agreed Dorothy. "His ain fowk, nithing bit skin and been. Pittin the fear o' death in a'b'dy. Knockin doon hale villages ..."

There was silence for a few moments while the queue considered the enormity of the former Romanian leader's crimes.

"Aye," said all five in unison. "He wis an affa Cockachesscoo."

They paused in their discussion of world affairs for a few moments when they fancied they heard a noise from inside the shop and strained for sounds of the bolts being slid back, but it was evidently a false alarm and they turned back to face each other again.

"Nivver mind Cockachesscoo," said Geneva. "Fit aboot that General boy doon aboot the Panama Canal? Yon's anither nickum, yon."

"Fa's that?" said Babbie.

"The boy," said Geneva, searching for a name. "Ye ken ... the boy. Fit d'ye ca' 'im? The boy wi the affa plooky face. Like a pizza."

"Oh, aye," said Babbie as light dawned, "that plooky-faced gadgie fae the Panama Canal. Him that wis holin up for Christmas in yon embassy in the lappa luxury."

"Lord," said Dorothy. "Fit some folk'll dee for a sup broth and a cracker."

They sat on the bench, staring blankly out into the street for a few moments, and it was Dorothy who broke the silence. "Ae wye and anither," she said, "hisn't it been a richt coorse year for tyrants?"

All five nodded sagely and silence fell again. "Aye," said Babbie presently, "there's the Panama boy. There's that lotta rogues in the Iron Curtain. And then there's peer aul Cockachesscoo ..."

"What a waste," said Virginia sadly.

"I know," said Claire Macfarlane, spotting a voice of compassion and sanity at last. "I quite agree with you, Virginia. Despite Ceausesçu's misdeeds, he was a human being, after all. No matter how black the mark against his name in the book of eternity, he deserved better than summary execution in cold blood. He deserved basic human rights, even although he denied them to so many of his countrymen. In executing him, his captors merely lowered themselves to his level. I don't believe we should ever sink to that, when human life is apparently worth so little. As you say so rightly, Virginia, what a waste!"

"No, no," said Virginia. "I meant what a waste o' a turkey. There's twa days aetin in a turkey, onywye. There she wis, Mrs Cockachesscoo, dishin up the sprouts.

"A knock at the front door. Then her and her man's taen oot in front o' the TV

59

cameras and BANG! Steen caul. And there, back in her kitchen, there's a turkey hardly startit."

"Ye're richt enough, Virginia," said Babbie. "There's plenty starvin bairnies in Africa could hiv been deein wi Mrs Cockachesscoo's turkey."

"Dinna spik ony mair aboot Christmas denners," said Flo, "for I'll jist start greetin. What a richt backside o' a Christmas denner we hid roon by. The worst I've ivver hid. I widna wish it on naeb'dy."

"Fit wye wis that?" said Geneva, and everyone else craned forward.

"Well," said Flo. "I telt Gibby on the Setterday that he should g'awa and get a turkey fae the butcher. I kent fine that there widna be mony turkeys left if I waitit ower lang, it bein turkey time and a'thing. So I says: 'If they hinna ony turkeys, jist get something else.'

"He comes back twinty minutes later, pleased as punch. He says: 'I'm hame,' he says.

"I says: 'I see that,' I says. 'Hiv ye got wir Christmas denner?'

"He says: 'They hidna ony turkeys left. Ye were richt enough.'

"I says: 'So ye got something else, like I telt ye?'

"He says: 'Aye.' Fit did he slap oot on the kitchen table? A packet o' puff pastry. Nithing else. Jist a packet o' pastry. By the time I got back til the butcher's, they were shut."

There was a mixed buzz of sympathy and hilarity among the assembly.

"Isn't that jist like my man?" said Flo. "Thick as clart in a bottle, that's Gibby. Nithing in his heid bit lice. Racks and racks o' dyeucks and chuckens and geese hingin up on hooks in the butcher's and he comes back wi a packet o' raw puff pastry."

"There's nae muckle ye can dee ti kittle up a half-pun slabba puff wi decorations, eether, is there?" said Dorothy.

"Well," said Babbie, "I think ye wis gey short-sichtit, Flo Spurtle, you and Gibby. I ken far there wis a turkey goin for nithing."

"Far wis that?" said Flo.

"Hardly a mark on it," said Babbie.

"Far aboot?" said Flo again.

Babbie grinned. "Ower at Mrs Cockachesscoo's."

Erchie plans his holidays

Episode 119 : February 3, 1990

WHEN Erchie Sotter visits the Stronach hairdresser and removes his bunnet, the barber is faced once again with a dome which sports hardly any hair at all. The ritual is always the same. "Well, Erchie," he says. "Short back and sides, or jist Pledge and a duster?"

"Jist a skite roon wi yer clippers," says Erchie, and the barber tries to spin a two-minute job to a full half-hour, for he knows that Erchie is there for company and conversation and certainly not for tonsorial skill. So the barber sits Erchie down and, with a flourish born of long practice, sweeps the nylon overall over Erchie's head and under his chin; pads a towel down the back of Erchie's shirt, and starts clipping.

"Well," said the barber, "hiv ye bookit yer hol'days yet?"

"Nae really," said Erchie. "I canna mak up ma mind atween three wikks in Hawaii or a fortnicht in Tahiti. Fit think ye yersel?"

"The fortnicht in Tahiti. I find it gets affa warm in Hawaii this time o' year."

"Exactly fit I wis thinkin," said Erchie. "If ye went til Hawaii, a' thon steel guitars and flooers roon aboot yer neck wid get on yer nerves afore lang, eh?"

"I suppose that," said the barber, clip-clip-clipping away at nothing at all.

"The great thing aboot Tahiti, amon a' thon bonnie dusky South Sea dames wi the grass skirts is that there's aye a chunce o' a fire." He savoured he prospect of grass ashes for a few moments before he came to himself again. "Far is't ye're headin for yersel this year?" he inquired of the barber. "Ye were in Canada last year, weren't ye?"

"Aye," said the barber, "seein the wife's relations. My wife his mair relations than onyb'dy else I ken. It's a dampt pest whiles, aye bidin wi yer wife's femly. Ye dinna get a minute til yersels. Still, it maks a holiday fine and cheap, nae peyin for nae hotels or nithing. There's jist whiles I funcy a change. I've taen hame a brochure this wikk. I thocht I funcied a river safari. Ye ken, oot amon a' thon monkeys and snakes up the Amazon."

"Mair o' yer wife's relations?" said Erchie.

The barber laughed. "Jist something different," he said.

"Well, ye widna catch me deid on that safari things," said Erchie, "nae efter fit happened til thon cannibal a puckle year back."

The barber paused in mid-clip. "Fit wis that?" he said.

"It wis in a' the papers," said Erchie. "This little cannibal boy decidit he wis fed up scuddlin aboot his ain mochey little village so he ups ae mornin and tells his cronies he wis awa on his holidays. Packs his case and a'thing. Zoom. He's awa."

"Ten days later, he's back. Ae leg missin. Three fingers gone aff his left hand."

"Awa," said the barber, aghast. "That's affa, that."

"I ken," said Erchie. "He said he wid nivver go self-caterin again."

Shopping's a struggle

Episode 120 : February 10, 1990

THE door at the Dreep household swung open, flooding the back yard with kitchen light. "Ye'd better tak the message-bag!" barked Aggie from somewhere inside. "Ye winna get far athoot a message-bag!"

"Yes, petal," said Walter, her husband, as he pulled on his parka. He raked around in the kitchen press; came upon a wicker basket which seemed to be unthreading itself in all sorts of strategic places, and stepped towards the door.

"Ye've got the list, hiv ye?" bawled Aggie from the depths of the house.

"Close to my heart, honeylumps," said Walter as he descended the first step.

"And ye'll nae forget nithing?" she shouted.

"Yer ivry wish is emblazoned across ma mind," said Walter, "a'thing fae cat food for Mr Tiddles til pints for yer steys, extra-large." Before Aggie could bawl again, Walter clattered shut the back door and trotted off, whistling, towards Stronach Emporium and General Stores.

WALTER surveyed the meagre selection of fresh produce with scarcely concealed apprehension. "Hiv ye ony cookin aeples?" he inquired timidly of shopkeeper Ebenezer Grip. "The wife's makkin an eve's puddin."

"Foo muckle's she needin?" said Ebenezer.

"Twa pun," said Walter, scanning his shopping list.

"Twa pun?" snorted Ebenezer. "Twa pun? Hiv you folk nivver heard o' the European Community? Hiv ye nae heard o' metricalisation? It'll seen be 1992 and you folk's still bidin in the last century. It's nae Twa Pun noo. Twa Pun went oot wi timmer bilers." Then, adopting the patronising tone of a long-suffering dominie, he added: "So, if it's nae twa pun, fit is it?"

Walter glanced nervously from side to side, trying to compose an appropriate answer. He hesitated. "Is it ... two pounds?"

"Kilograms," sighed Ebenezer. "It's kilograms. Yer wife needs a kilogram o' cookin aeples."

"Oh, OK," said Walter.

"And I hinna got neen," said Ebenezer. "This is nae a good time for cookin aeples. So she'll hae ti tak eaters instead. They're the same difference." And Ebenezer selected five of his scabbiest French Golden Delicious, dumped them into a brown paper bag and whirled and twisted it shut with the practised flourish of country shopkeepers. He clattered them down on the counter.

Then he put both hands on the counter and stared fixedly at Walter, almost daring him to ask for something else.

Walter looked nervously at the pyokie of apples, then glanced up to meet Ebenezer's piercing glower briefly before returning to his list.

"We're needin a sup milk, as weel," he said. "We'll be haein porridge the nicht, likely. And Mr Tiddles is turnin most affa thirsty."

"How much?" said Ebenezer.

"Oh, *affa* thirsty," said Walter.

"Nae yer flechy cat," said Ebenezer. "Foo much milk are ye needin?"

"A pint," said Walter.

"Nae a pint," said Ebenezer.

"Nae a pint?" said Walter.

"Nae a pint," said Ebenezer, shaking his head.

Walter paused to think for a few moments. "Well, hiv ye twa half-pints?" he suggested brightly.

"Fit I'm sayin," said Ebenezer, "is that we dinna deal in pints nae mair. It's litres noo. Ye'll hae ti tak a half-litre o' milk." And he plucked a carton from a green plastic crate on the floor next to him and dumped it on the counter next to the apples. "Is that yer lot?" he asked.

"No," said Walter. "The wife's needin some yalla ribbon for rowin up a birthday present for wir niece."

"How much is she wintin?" said Ebenezer.

By this time, though, Walter was wise to Ebenezer and he hesitated. He held out his hands as if describing the fictional fish so beloved of unsuccessful anglers.

"Aboot that much," he said.

"And foo much is that much?" said Ebenezer.

"... That ... depends," said Walter.

"On fit?" said Ebenezer.

"On ... foo pricey it is."

"It's the best-quality stuff," said Ebenezer. "There's nae rubbish in this shop." He took his hook-pole and lifted a cardboard box down from the very top shelf at the back of the shop. He set the box down on the counter and blew across the top of it, raising such a cloud of dust that the shafts of winter-dawn sunlight coming through the windows were almost palpable.

"Michty," coughed Walter, "there's surely nae muckle call in Stronach for yalla ribbon." But Ebenezer ignored him and lifted the top of the box. He began raking around inside and pulled out the card of yellow.

"It's a bittie pricey, mind," he said. "Ye pey for the best o' modrin produce."

"How much?" said Walter.

"I've left ma glesses ben in the back shop," said Ebenezer, pushing the box towards Walter. "Here. It'll be written on the front."

Walter peered at the faint pencil markings on the end of the box for a few seconds.

"Well, foo muckle is't?" said Ebenezer impatiently.

Walter looked up.

"Half a croon a yard."

Marriage guidance

Episode 121 : February 17, 1990

ACROSS at the bar, on their regular Thursday-evening sortie to the Stronach Arms, Walter Dreep and Sandy Brose looked anything but happy, contented pubgoers. They stared gloomily into their pints.

"Your trouble, Wattie," observed Sandy, "is that ye've nae sensa humour. Ye canna lach at life's misfortunes. Ye dinna roll wi the punches."

"You've obviously nae been on the wrang end o' a punch fae my Aggie," said Walter. "Nae sensa humour? Fit hiv I for lachin at?"

"Well," said Sandy, "I've a rare cure. It works ivry time for me." He leaned closer to Walter conspiratorially and dropped his voice to a loud whisper. "I goes hame til the wife. I pits ma airms roon aboot her and I nuzzles intil her neck. I blaws in her lugs and I says: 'Hullo, darlin. Tarzan's hame.' "

"Tarzan's hame," repeated Walter, taking a mental note.

Sandy nodded. "Tarzan's hame. Then I waltzes her roon aboot the kitchen; I plants a great big smacker o' a kiss on her ruby-red lips; I rins ma fingers doon her spine, and she jist melts intil ma airms."

"Waltz, smacker, fingers and melts," noted Walter.

Warming to his task, Sandy continued: "Then, efter a' that, she forgets that she's ill-natered. She's putty in yer hands. I rest ma case."

"Ye ken this," said Walter, brightening, "that sounds the business, richt enough. I'll try that. I'll fairly try that."

NEXT Thursday, Walter and Sandy were back at their appointed time at the barstools.

"Well," said Sandy. "How did ye get on?"

"Sandy," said Walter, "I maun buy ye yer pint the nicht. Yer tip workit a treat. I raced in through the back door. I ran ma airms roon aboot her. 'Tazan's hame,' I says. I waltzed her roon aboot the kitchen. I plantit the smacker. I ran ma fingers up and doon lik playin a fiddle. She fairly meltit intil ma airms, jist lik ye said."

"Fit did I tell ye?" said Sandy, beaming. "A sensa humour's a great thing. Be lik me. Lach at life. Enjoy yersel. Hiv ye learned yer lesson now, div ye think?"

"Oh, aye," said Walter. "I've fairly learned ma lesson fae ye. A sensa humour's fit I need. You fairly learned me that. And I'll tell ye something else."

"Fit's that?" said Sandy.

"That's lovely kitchen units ye've got."

Teenager troubles

Episode 122 : February 24, 1990

A RAP and clatter on the inside of the window told almost half of Stronach how annoyed Babbie Girn was. A gang of teenagers had been playing football in the street outside her house. Their ball had sailed through the air after a particularly difficult shot and had landed in her garden.

One lad had louped the fence and had battered his way through the shrubs and roses to retrieve it and Babbie was none too pleased.

She knocked furiously on the glass again. "Get yer big feet affa my roses, ye big ugly vratch!" she roared. "Oota my gairden afore I come and heat yer backside! Ye're nae ower big for a skelpit dock!"

The boy retrieved his ball at lightning speed and jumped back over the fence twice as quickly as he had jumped in and raced away with his mates to find another corner of the village for their kickabout. Babbie's reputation still carries some weight with the village small fry.

Babbie let the curtains return to perpendicular and turned back into the room. "Did ye see that?" she asked of Virginia Huffie, who had dropped in for a fly-cup. "Nae mainners nooadays. If we'd tried that in my young day, we'd hiv been shot on the spot. And then far wid we hiv been?"

"Deid," said Virginia.

"Exactly," said Babbie. "There's nae respeck for naeb'dy's property nae mair. They go spaddin a' ower yer bonny gairden and think nithing o't. I've a good mind ti report the hale dampt lot o' them. Nae respeck. Nae respeck ava."

"Calm doon now," soothed Virginia. "Gettin yersel workit up's nae the answer. Fit aboot takkin a stroll doon til the tearoom this efterneen for a cuppie o' tea and a Kit Kat? We can tak the papers for a good lang read and it'll get ye oot o' the hoose."

D OWN at the tearoom, things were busy. The Sunday winter sunshine had brought carloads of Aberdonians out for their first Sunday drive of the year.

And what happened? Babbie and Virginia were horrified to find that the only two empty seats were at a table for four ... and that the other two places were taken by the footballing teenager and his 14-year-old girlfriend.

"Oh me," said Virginia, biting her lip. "Maybe we'd hiv been better bidin at hame efter a'."

"Dash the bit," said Babbie, striding up to the table and glowering hotly at the boy. "I'm nae bein kept fae a fly-cup by some wee ... *nyaff*!" She shot the "nyaff" with especial venom at the teenager.

"Fit aboot a cuppie o' tea and a fine piece?" suggested Virginia, leaning forward and whispering. "I'll pey."

"Not at all," said Babbie, reaching into the pockets of her voluminous tweed coat for her purse. She fumbled for a few seconds almost down about her knees until she located it, then drew it out with a flourish. "It's my shottie. Fit will ye hae?"

"You decide," said Virginia. "I like a surprise." And Babbie marched off towards the self-service counter intending to purchase two cups of strong tea and two Kit Kats.

At the counter, she turned back towards Virginia and called: "There's an affa funny smell in here ivnoo." And she sniffed theatrically in mid-air, as if trying to detect the undetectable. "Aye," she said presently. "I believe it's the smell o' *impidence.*"

The young buck at the table smiled an easy, swaggery smile and shifted into a slouching position.

Babbie returned with two cups, clattered them down on the table, shot another glower at the teenagers and sat down, thrusting the newspaper intoVirginia's hands. "Here ye go," she said. "Tak a read o' that. At least you can read. Unlike ... *some folk.*" She shot the "some folk" towards the teenagers with venom anew.

Virginia obeyed meekly and Babbie got out her Sunday paper and opened it full sail, the better to screen out the horrendous, defiant, chewing faces at the other side of the table.

After a few minutes, she reached round from behind her paper, still reading, to retrieve her Kit Kat from her saucer.

There was no Kit Kat.

She folded down the top of her paper and stared at the saucer. It was empty. She looked up at the teenager, still lounging and slouching, snarling and chewing. In his own saucer, was a screwed-up ball of red wrapper and silver paper.

It was a Kit Kat wrapper.

Babbie's eyes narrowed. She said nothing but, instead, stretched forward to the young man's girlfriend, snatched an unopened Mars Bar from the side of the girl's mug of coffee, tore off the wrapper, and took a huge, gargantuan bite, stuffing as much as she could into her mouth at one go.

She sat there chewing defiantly — as defiant as the teenagers had been only a few moments before. Only now they were aghast; their jaws dropped.

Through mouthfuls of caramel, nougat and thick, thick chocolate, Babbie spat: "Aye, ye dinna like it fin the tables is turned, eh? Ye dinna like it fin ither folk plays ye at yer ain game. You young folk nooadays, ye're a dampt disgrace. Nae mainners. Nae courtesy. Nae respeck."

"Mrs Girn," called the woman at the till.

Babbie looked round. The woman was waving two Kit Kats.

"Mrs Girn, ye took yer teas, bit ye forgot yer pieces."

Tiffs à la Spurtle

Episode 125 : March 17, 1990

AN ANGRY Flo Spurtle spun on her heels and headed for the living-room door. Before she left, she turned to address her husband, Gibby, and her sister.

"As far as you lot's concerned, I'm jist a bloomin eediot," she howled. "I'm a bloomin gype roon aboot here. Ye'd be gey peer craiteries if ye hidna me ti lach at. Well lach awa! See if I care! I'm awa upstairs for a bath! I'll maybe droon masel while I'm at it. Save us a' a lotta pain and misery! Ye can baith mak yer ain tea!"

And she slammed the door shut and clumped up the stairs, leaving Gibby and his sister-in-law staring at each other, incredulous.

"She's a bittie upset," observed Gibby.

"Upset?" said Flo's sister. "She sounds near suicidal. Fit hiv you twa been argyin aboot this time?"

"Nae nithing, really," said Gibby sheepishly. Then he thought for a moment. "I did kinda hint she'd let hersel go since the baby wis born."

"Hint?" said Flo's sister.

"I said I'd seen better-lookin things rollin in a midden," said Gibby. He considered for a few moments, then looked up. "She didna tak it affa weel."

Flo's sister went and got their coats. "I think you and me's got some serious spikkin in front o's," she said. "Here. Tak yer coat. It's caul ootside and we're awa for a walk."

"She's jist richt aff me a'thegither," said Gibby, pulling on his anorak. "She's nae time for me. I nivver get a look in. I think there's somebody else."

"Of course there's somebody else," said Flo's sister. "There's the baby. That's a big responsibility for ony young mum."

"Na, na," said Gibby. "I mean ... ye ken ... somebody else. Somebody's keepin her feeties toastit. Somebody's gettin his eggs biled, and nae mistake."

"Awa and bile yer ain eggs," said Flo's sister, pushing Gibby towards the door. "That's a lotta nonsense, and weel ye ken't."

"The coalman's got an affa cheesy grin on him nooadays," said Gibby. "And there's aye a puckle black marks on the doorknobs ivry ither Thursday."

"Get oot that bloomin door," said Flo's sister. As Gibby stumbled forward down the steps, she called back inside: "Flo! Gibby and me's awa for a walk! It's a bonny aifterneen. We'll be back in a coupla oors." And she clattered the door shut.

Upstairs, Flo sank a little deeper into the luxuriously foamy bath she had run herself. She sighed a deep and satisfying sigh and idly rubbed the suds into her shoulders. She hummed a little tune softly, then sighed again. Then she dozed, ever so gently, and fell fast asleep.

IT WAS the squeak of the garden gate that woke her. The bathwater was cool; almost cold. As she jerked awake, the water splashed about her and, on tiptoe, she looked out the skylight on to the street below.

The Hydro Board van had parked outside, and the meter-reader was striding towards the Spurtle abode. It was the over-chatty meter-reader; the one who scrounged cups of tea and who made boring conversation; the one who scoured the house until he found you.

There was a sharp rap at the front door and the handle was tried almost instantly. The door was locked. Now, the question was, had Gibby and her sister locked the back door?

Probably not.

Desperate to stop him coming in, Flo bounded out of the bathroom, down the stairs two at a time and raced for the back door. She was racing along the lobby when, suddenly, she realised she was stark naked.

Not a stitch on.

Birthday suit.

Nude.

Panicking, she dived into the nearest cupboard; the one under the stairs. She slammed the door shut behind her and, panting, listened intently. She heard the clump of his heavy boots going along the back path towards the back door.

The back door handle turned . . . and nothing more. Her sister surely *had* locked the door. Flo sighed with relief; waited a few more seconds until she thought he must have gone away; sighed again, and pushed on the inside of the cupboard door. It was jammed tight.

JUST a few minutes later, the back door was unlocked and opened and Flo held her breath. She didn't know it, but this time it was Gibby and her sister, back from their stroll. They thumped their feet to generate warmth after the March cold. Flo could hear them only too well.

As Flo's sister hung up their coats, Gibby picked up the postcard slid under the door by the meter-reader, asking for a self-reading.

"So I hope we've finally got rid o' this notion that Flo's takkin up wi anither man," said Flo's sister.

"Michty aye," said Gibby, "I wis oot o' order on that score." And he found a pen and paper and walked towards the meter cupboard under the stairs, intending to take the reading while it was fresh in his mind.

He tugged open the door and there, squatting on the floor, was Flo, naked as the day she was born.

They stared at each other, open-mouthed, for a few seconds. It was Flo who broke the silence.

"Oh," she said. "It's you."

Then, summoning all the dignity she could muster, she added, by way of explanation:

"I wis expectin the meter-reader."

Honeymoon emergency

Episode 126 : March 24, 1990

The March rain was lashing and the gales blasting all over the Howe of Stronach, and not even the most dedicated drinker had ventured out for a Friday-evening pint at the Stronach Arms.

The embers were glowing red and sinking low as early as 7.30, and only Erchie Sotter was left propped against the bar, nursing a golden stain at the bottom of his glass and mightily upset that there was no one to buy him his next drink.

He was chatting with John the barman when suddenly the door blew open and the wintry blast from outside whistled through the bar, carrying with it rain, cigarette packets, sweetie papers ... and a young man and woman who were absolutely drenched.

"Michty me," said John the barman, coming out from behind the bar to close the door while the young couple stamped the rain from their coats.

"Mochey nicht," observed Erchie.

"Indeed," said the young man. "Not a good night for a car to break down three miles up the glen."

"And certainly not a good wedding night," said the young woman.

"Weel, losh be here," said Erchie sunnily, and slipping down from his barstool. "Ye werena mairriet the day, were ye?" The young couple looked at each other, smiled, threw an arm round each other and nodded.

"Oh, bit that calls for a drink," said Erchie. "And mine's a Macallan."

"Actually," said the young man. "We're tired, soaking and hungry. We just want a simple snack; a phone to call ahead to the hotel where we're meant to be spending our first night in the honeymoon suite, and a room for the night here, if that's possible."

John nodded and directed them towards the dining-room, where they sat down (the young man checking his wallet for money), obviously very much in love.

NEXT morning, up in the main guest room, the young couple were awake bright and early. The young man was in the bath, singing loudly and merrily, while the young woman was propped up on the pillows in the bed, smiling dreamily to herself.

The man reappeared from the bathroom, surprised to find his wife still in bed, and slipped out of his dressing-gown to begin getting dressed.

"You'd better hurry, dear, if you're coming down to breakfast. I think they'll probably be stopping serving breakfasts very soon." He looked at his watch. "It's nine o'clock already."

"Just let me lie here for a wee while yet," she sighed. "It's just too peaceful for words. And it's not every morning that's your first morning of marriage. Just let me lie here and appreciate it. I want to have memories of this for ever."

"All right," he said. "If that's what you want."

"Just one other thing," she said. He sat on the edge of the bed.

"Anything," he said, stroking her hair.

"Would you pass me my cigarettes? I'll be down in twenty minutes."

DOWNSTAIRS a few minutes later, Erchie was walking in through the hotel lobby for his morning scrounge of a bowl of Ricicles when, through the dining-room door, he spotted the young man. He stopped and wandered up to the door, pushing it slightly farther ajar.

"Aye aye, min," he said. The young man looked up from his orange juice and toast and Erchie winked heavily at him.

"Ye got slept a'richt, did ye?" said Erchie, winking again, pushing the door fully open and stepping into the dining-room. "Ye're gey tired-lookin," and he winked yet again.

The young man began to feel a little uncomfortable and he fixed his stare on his toast and on his "P and J". When he looked up again, Erchie was seating himself at the same table.

"Comfy bed, wis't?" said Erchie. "Nae lumpy or nithing? I mean, ye got a good nicht's sleep?" The young man raised his head, smiled a wan smile and returned to reading his paper. Evidently, he was not going to be drawn on his nocturnal activities, and Erchie sat back for a few moments to consider a new strategy.

"So ye're doon for yer breakfast yersel this mornin, are ye?" said Erchie.

The young man looked around the table in a pronounced manner, lifting the condiments, the toast-rack and the teapot, as if searching for some small trinket. He was perfectly obviously by himself and the stupidity of Erchie's question rankled a little.

"Apparently, I am," he said, and he rustled his paper and went back to reading about Botriphnie WRI's lemon-curd competition.

Erchie sat back for another few moments. Then he tried again. "A richt fine hotel, this," he said, looking around the dining-room. "Richt quaet rooms they've got. Nae nithing ti bother ony guests. Aye, guests get a richt quaet nicht's sleep at this hotel."

But the young man was not to be drawn, so Erchie helped himself to a slice of toast, oblivious to the young man's glare, and nibbled idly on the corner for a few moments.

"Far's the dame, than?" he said.

"I beg your pardon?" said the young man, aghast.

"The dame. The bitta stuff. Yer wife. Far is she?"

"Actually," said the young man, folding his paper with scarcely concealed irritation, "if you must know, she's lying upstairs in bed, smoking."

A look of delight crossed Erchie's face and he leaned across and clapped the young man hard on the back.

"That's ma loon!" he said. "Good for you!

"Leave them rikkin!"

A question of grammar

Episode 128 : April 7, 1990

F OR all her forward-thinking ideas in education, Miss Euphemia Pink, of Primary Five at Stronach Primary School, still has an element of the traditionalist about her. While other teachers have broken away from timestables, handwriting and basic grammar, Miss Pink still manages to sneak in a few classes in the three Rs.

"This will stand you in good stead in years to come," she tells the class when they start groaning. "The day will come when you will thank me for drumming this into you. Far too many of you are stuck when your calculator batteries run out or when you run up against a moderately difficult three-syllable word."

So the class get out their exercise books and pencils and begin scribbling and calculating.

However, traditionalist though she is, Miss Pink tries her best to make these lessons fun, and in last Monday afternoon's lesson in grammar, she was trying to explain the concept of the adjective.

"They are the describing words of the English language," she told the class. "They modify and expand nouns — the *thing* words — by adding to our understanding of them." The blank looks on much of the class told her she was beginning to leave them behind, so she rethought her strategy.

"For instance," she said. "The word 'lovely' is an adjective. We can have a 'lovely' flower or a 'lovely' car ..."

"Or a 'lovely' plate of skirkie and custard," offered Wayne Spurtle.

"Yes, Wayne," said Miss Pink. "That is true, but please don't be stupid. Only an idiot would eat skirlie and custard in the same plate." As the rest of the class erupted into laughter, Wayne sat fuming.

"All right! All right!" said Miss Pink, calming them down. "We'll try this another way. I want you to give me a sentence with the word 'lovely' appearing twice. Then you'll see what adjectives are."

After a few seconds' thought, a few hands went up.

"Yes, Sharon Grip," said Miss Pink. "What's your sentence?"

"Please, Miss," said Sharon, "we went out for a picnic at my grandma's at Turriff yesterday and we had a *lovely* time eating her *lovely* home-baking."

Miss Pink smiled benignly at this somewhat pedestrian sentence. "Yes, Sharon," she said. "That certainly fits the bill. Well done. Now, anyone else?"

She scanned the class again and spotted a small, scruffy-looking lad in a Rangers shirt. "Yes, George," she said. "What's your sentence?"

"Please, Miss," said George, "I wis watching *lovely* Rangers on the TV yesterday and they had a *lovely* win over that nasty, nasty bunch of Celtic butchers."

"Yes, George," said Miss Pink, "trust you to get football into it somewhere. Nevertheless, that's a good example of a two-adjective sentence. Well done."

And Miss Pink scanned the class for a third time. However, only Wayne was left with his hand up, fingers snapping furiously. Evidently backed into a corner, Miss Pink sighed. "Yes, Wayne," she said, "bless this assembled multitude with your sentence ... and please stop snapping your fingers like that. I'm not deaf, you know."

"Please, Miss. Please, Miss," snapped Wayne. "My cousin wis oot wi her boyfriend a coupla wikks ago."

Miss Pink looked expectantly at Wayne, and the rest of the class were intrigued, too. After a few moments' silence had passed, Miss Pink felt obliged to inquire further. "Go on," she said. "what happened to the *lovely*?"

"Well," said Wayne, "now ma cousin's found oot that she's pregment. She's expectin a baby and her nae mairriet nor nithing."

Miss Pink blushed a fetching shade of puce, coughed in a mildly embarrassed fashion and bade Wayne continue.

"Well," said Wayne, "she went hame last nicht and telt her aul man. He wisna affa pleased."

"I don't imagine her father would be entirely ecstatic, no," said Miss Pink. "However, these melodramas are none of our concern at present. I am trying to run a class in basic English grammar, not interpersonal relationships. Wayne, I'm sure we'll get to the point of this eventually, but meanwhile we're sitting here patiently awaiting your sentence with the two *lovelies* in it."

"Well," said Wayne, "that's jist it. She went hame and telt her faither and he shouted at her: 'Fit! Ye're sixteen and ye're pregment?

" Then he fell in a heap and he said: 'Well, that's *lovely*, jist bloomin *lovely*.' "

A new story

The green-eyed monster

G IBBY slipped his piecebag off his shoulder and dropped it on the floor inside the back door. He stretched his arms wide and yawned, for it had been an exhausting day in the garden at Crochlie Neuk. The dockens at the back of the outhouses had been especially tenacious and the heat hadn't agreed with him. He wondered whether he might have a touch of sunstroke.

He walked through to the kitchen, tilted the plastic basin in the sink on its end and turned on the hot tap. He yawned again, rubbed an aching left shoulder and peered at his tanned, sweat-stained face in the mirror on the far wall.

"Aye, Gibby," he mused. "Ye've fairly taen the sun the day. Better than a hale wikk in Majorca." He admired the lobster-pink forehead and the red bulb that was his nose. "They'll be ca'in ye Rudolph at the pubbie the nicht."

He splashed his face with water from cupped hands and felt the better for it. He grasped for the towel that was held normally on the handle of the cooker grill but found nothing. He opened his eyes and blinked his way round the room until he found a teatowel on the back of one of the kitchen chairs, so he used that instead. Flo didn't like it, he knew, but Flo wouldn't know.

And that was when he heard the voices from the front room. And there was laughter. Girlish laughter. And the hearty laughing of a man.

Gibby listened for a few moments, puzzled. Then he pushed open the door and saw Flo sitting on the sofa and Bob, the village milkman, standing in the centre of the room. Flo looked round quickly and Bob looked up.

"Oh, hullo, Gibby," said Flo, sitting forward. "I didna hear ye come in. Yer tea winna be lang."

"Aye, Gibby," said Bob, reaching for his bag of money and the payment book. "It must be rare haein yer tea made for ye ilky nicht. I'm awa hame til a caul hoosie and a tinnie o' beans. Still, that's a bachelor's lot, I suppose."

"I suppose," said Gibby.

"Well, Flo," said Bob, "I'll awa. Same time next wikk?"

"Fairly, Bob," said Flo, standing up. "I'm lookin forward til't. Ye fairly mak peyin a bill a lach."

Gibby turned and walked back into the kitchen while Flo escorted Bob out through the front door. Gibby stood rinsing dishes at the kitchen sink, which was something he didn't normally do, but something had put the notion in his head so he just stood there, idly swilling teacups in the water and running the hot tap on them.

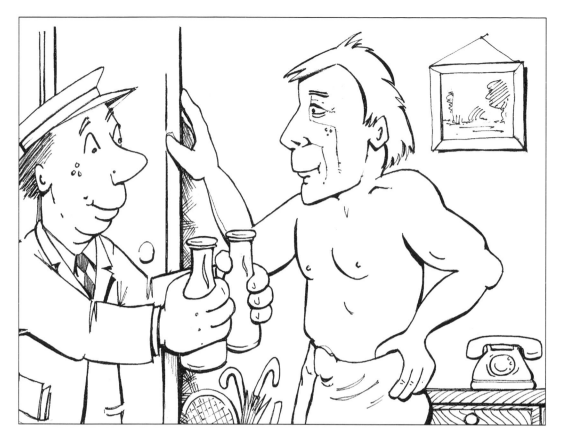

There was more laughter from the front door, then a toot of a van followed by the sound of the door closing. Presently, Flo was in the kitchen still with a faint smile on her face and obviously looking for something to do.

"I've deen yer dishes," said Gibby, without looking round. "Twa cups, I see."

"Twa cups," confirmed Flo. "And twa speens and twa plates that hid twa pieces on them. Bob likes a fly cup at the end o' his rounds, so I asked him in for a fly. Ye surely dinna mind that. It canna be easy bidin himsel, him bein a bachelor. He needs a bit o' lookin efter, I aye think. He aye looks like he's needin taen in hand."

"That's his choice," said Gibby, reaching for the teatowel that, only moments before, he had used to dry his hands. He lifted one of the cups and began drying it. "It's his choice ti bide single and funcy-free, jist as it's my choice ti hae a wife."

"Oh, Bob's a richt lach," said Flo, smiling as she remembered some of the jokes she had just heard. "He's aye got stories. Aye jokin and kiddin on. I sometimes think ye could spend a hale day and a hale nicht wi Bob and nae hear the same joke twice. What a lach he is. They should hae him on the National Health. The illness rates in the country wid drap in nae time ata. He's a richt tonic."

"Is that so?" said Gibby, clattering another cup down on the worktop.

But Flo was oblivious. "I could listen til him a' day," she said fondly. "A' the time I've kent him, he's nivver telt the same story twice. I dinna ken how he minds them a'. What a memory he must hae. He's really entertainin. Hiv ye heard the joke aboot...?"

"I prefer the TV masel," said Gibby, finishing drying the dishes and walking past Flo to put away the cups and plates. Flo stared at him as he passed. Then she thought for a few moments.

"You're in a gey funny humour, chummie," she said. "Ye're nae jealous, Gibby, are ye?"

Gibby didn't look round. "I've nithing for bein jealous aboot," he said, still with his back to Flo. "I'd be an eediot bein jealous o' nithing ata. So I'm nae." He walked back to the sink. "Of coorse," he said. "I canna say fit wid happen if I *did* hae something ti be jealous aboot." Then he turned and looked straight at her. "Can I?" he said.

"Now ye're jist bein silly," snapped Flo. "A fly cup? Twa custard creams and a cup o' tea? Ye're nae jealous o' that?"

Gibby turned round. "And a' this entertainin? Bob this. Bob that. What a lach Bob is. Bob's really entertainin. Bob's great. I could listen til Bob a' day. Bob, Bob, Bob. There's mair Bob, Bob, Bobbin goin on in here than a hale flock o' reid robins manage in a hunder Christmases."

"Ye *are* jealous," said Flo. She walked forward and stood side on to Gibby, who stood staring into the wall cupboard. "Ye're nae jealous, Gibby, are ye?" she said, peering up at his face.

Gibby turned his head and looked at her. "Of coorse I'm jealous," he said. "I come hame efter a hard day diggin the biggest gairden in Stronach. I'm sair. I'm filthy. I'm het. I'm hungry. And ma wife's sittin in ma front room lachin wi the milkie ower tea and biscuits. The milkie's gettin treatment *I* dinna get in ma ain hoose. Of coorse I'm bliddy jealous."

Flo walked to the table in the centre of the kitchen. "Well, I've nivver heard nithing so dampt silly in a' ma born days," she said. "Ma man's jealous o' the milkie. Twa custard creams and a cup o' tea and he's jealous. What a state ye'd be in if it wis onything serious."

"And it's nae?"

"Growe up, Gibby," snorted Flo. "Ye're in one o' yer contermacious moods and I canna win. We'll jist stop this conversation afore it starts. Fit are ye needin for yer tea?"

"Twa custard creams," said Gibby.

TEATIME passed in silence but for the noise of Wayne chawing at bread and jam with his mouth open and Cassandra spreading chocolate sponge everywhere near her mouth except inside it and laughing with delight.

But Gibby and Flo ignored her. They stared at their boiled ham and tomatoes and ate wordlessly. Wayne was puzzled, but said nothing and reached for more bread. Cassandra was just enjoying the feel of all that chocolate on her face.

Flo stood up at the end of the meal and gathered all the dirty dishes to the sink. Wayne helped, for Wayne suspected that he might have done something wrong, and had learned through long practice that helping round the house usually lessened the punishment. He studied his mother and father while he put away the butter dish, and the bottle of tomato ketchup and the tin of syrup. Something was definitely awry.

"I'll pit Cassandra til her bed," he offered.

"It's a bit early for her bed yet," said Flo flatly.

"Well I'll play a game wi her up the stairs," offered Wayne. He took his little sister in his bosie and lifted her on to the floor, then he took her hand and led her out of the kitchen. "Ta-ta," giggled Cassandra through layers of dried chocolate icing. "Ta-ta."

But Gibby and Flo didn't respond and, a few moments later, they were alone in the kitchen.

"He's a good loon, that," said Flo presently.

"Taks efter his dad," said Gibby.

"D'ye think he noticed?" said Flo.

"Noticed fit?"

"Yer funny humour. Yer sulkin."

"It's nae *my* funny humour," said Gibby. "I'm the same as ivver. In the circumstances."

Flo walked back to the kitchen table and ruffled her husband's hair. "Ye big feel clort," she said. "I'm affa flattered that ye're jealous, bit what a lotta nonsense. He's the milkman. He tells a funny story. He's entertainin. He's a lach. Bit that's a' he is." Gibby seemed unconvinced, so she ruffled his hair again while she thought of something new to say.

"Gibby," she said, with a note of desperation in her voice. "He's as ugly as a stirk's dowp. He's nae beefcake, if that's fit ye're thinkin. He's nae a pin-up, by ony stretch o' the imagination. Lord, why d'ye think he's still single at thirty-five? Naeb'dy'll hae him."

Gibby seemed unconvinced, but willing to be persuaded. He looked up at Flo and waited for her to continue.

"Gibby," she said. "How could I see by you? Ye've got the biggest muscles in the howe. Ye look like a bodybuilder that weemin throw themsels at. Ye're the nearest thing this place his got til Arnold Schwarzenegger," she said, ruffling his hair again.

"Considerin the competition's Erchie Sotter and Walter Dreep, that's nae sayin much," mumbled Gibby.

Flo pulled a seat up next to Gibby and sat down beside him. She put an arm round his shoulders. "I'd need ma heid lookin fan I've got the best-lookin bloke for miles roon a' till masel." She ruffled his hair yet again. "Ma big gairdnin man. Ma Piercy Thrower." Then she paused and leaned forward to whisper: "How aboot some propagation the nicht?"

Gibby beamed from ear to ear, then his face became serious. "I'm sorry," he said. "Nae propagatin the nicht. Quite impossible. There's nae an R in the month."

Flo laughed uproariously. "That's my Gibby," she said, pinching his cheek. "A jealous clort, bit that's my Gibby."

"I'll help ye wash the dishes," said Gibby, smiling and standing up, and Flo handed him a teatowel. They stood for a few moments washing and drying the tea dishes then, as Flo wiped down the draining board, she said: "Ye ken, Gibby, jokin apart, this jealousy o' yours sometimes worries me. Ye've aye been jealous, ivver since we wis coortin, bit ye've been gettin terrible jealous lately. I've nivver seen ye like this. This jealousy'll land ye in trouble some day. Mark my words."

"Only because I've got something that needs keepin an eye on," said Gibby, putting his arms round his wife's middle and giving her a peck on the cheek. "I'm thinkin o' makkin up a sign for ye. 'Property of Gilbert A. Spurtle. Keep Aff.' Fit d'ye think?"

"It's got a ring til it," agreed Flo. "Wid it be a big sign? I mean, wid I get through doors wi it? Or wid it be jist a little sign? Sma and tasteful, a bit like masel?"

And now it was Gibby's turn to laugh. "Wid ye like ti hear ma good news?" he said.

"I like hearin ony good news," said Flo.

"I'm bein put on a course for gairdnin management," said Gibby, and Flo looked blank. "Ye ken fit that means?" he said.

"It's so ye can manage a gairden?" offered Flo.

"Well, aye," said Gibby, "bit it means ma job's secure. It means I've passed ma probation. It means ma job as the gairdener at Crochlie Neuk must be permanent, for they widna pit me awa on a wikk's course til Edinburgh if they were peyin me aff, wid they?"

And suddenly Flo, too, grasped the enormity of what had happened. She beamed broadly then flung her arms round Gibby. "Gibby, that's super," she said. "A richt job efter a' this time. Ye're a workin man again. Ye're takkin hame a wage."

"And now I'll hae a professional qualification ahen me," said Gibby, and he puffed out his chest. "I winna be jist an odd-job man. I winna be jist a gairdnin labourer, spaddin on dung and cuttin grass. I'll be a professional horticulturalist. I'll hae a certificate up on ma wa. A diploma, jist like the doctor's got at the surgery. Gilbert A. Spurtle. Diploma in Garden Management. I can jist see it noo."

"Aye, well, dinna rin afore ye're walkin," said Flo. "Ye've a wikk's course yet. In Edinburgh? My my. Ma man's a student." And she thought for a few moments. "They surely think a lot o' ye, Gibby. Pittin you awa on a course winna be cheap. It's costin them money. They must be really pleased wi ye. They must think ye're a good investment."

"They must," said Gibby, "mustn't they?"

Flo planted a kiss on his cheek. "Dinna you come back packit wi funcy ideas," she said. "Jist you come back the same Gibby and I'll be fine pleased, pass or fail."

"Failure's nivver entered ma heid," said Gibby. "I'll be top o' the class. Jist you wait. I'll hae that diploma up on ma wa yet. I winna let ye doon."

"Ye've nivver let me doon, Gibby," said Flo. "Nae a' that time ye hidna a job. Nae even fan ye thocht ye'd nivver hae a job again. Nae nivver. I kent yer time wid come."

"And now it's come," said Gibby. "Ma time's come. Ma boat's sailed in at last. Lady Fortune's smilin at me. The road's risin ti meet me. Ma path o' destiny is glowin wi good fortune. Ma ..."

And Flo silenced him with a long, long kiss.

"...and ye ken fit else?" said Gibby, breaking off.

"Fit else?" smiled Flo.

"Milkies dinna get diplomas."

THE paperwork arrived a few days later confirming, indeed, that Gilbert Alexander Spurtle had been nominated to attend a short residential vocational course in horticultural management at a college in Edinburgh. Gibby read it and re-read it. And Flo read it and re-read it and couldn't believe that Gibby had landed so squarely on his feet.

She brought the case down from the top of the wardrobe and began packing his clothes when he had three days still to go before departure. She packed the case then unpacked it and ironed some of the clothes again, just to be sure. You couldn't be too careful, she decided. Edinburgh was a gey toffee place and Gibby had to make a good impression. He was to be the neatest student of gardening management the college had seen.

Gibby seemed different as the appointed day drew near. More confident. More self-assured. Walking a little taller. Relaxing and laughing more. More even-tempered with the children, and Flo revelled in it. This was how families were supposed to be, she thought. And she couldn't get enough of it. If this was what the prospect of a course did for Gibby, he could go on a course every month as far as she was concerned. She hadn't laughed so much in ages.

"Now," said Gibby on the evening before departure, "I'm needin a serious word wi you, madam."

"And fit's that?" said Flo, tucking his one and only suit inside a suit-hanger and zipping up the front.

Gibby took her by the shoulder and gently turned her round to face him. "Fan the master o' the house is awa in the big city, he disna wint ither folk snuffin aboot this hoose."

"No?" said Flo.

"No," said Gibby. "Nae pensioners. Nae larry-drivers. Nae odd-job men."

"And especially nae milkies?" said Flo.

"Especially nae milkies ca'ed Bob," said Gibby emphatically. "Milkies is oot o' the question. No Bobs allowed. This hale hoose is to be a Bob-free zone.

Understood? Hiv I got ma message through til ye? His that registered inside that bonnie heid?"

"Message received and understood," said Flo, saluting. "Gie's a kiss, ye good-lookin devil."

GIBBY was up at the first sign of dawn, doing his 15th check on his packing then heading for the bathroom for his shower. Flo got up to make him a special send-off breakfast of bacon, sausages, tomatoes, scrambled eggs and fried bread, because "Edinburgh's a lang wye on the train and it'll be the last square meal ye'll hae for a wikk".

Gibby was walking downstairs from the bathroom with only a towel round his waist when the letterbox rapped gently. He looked at his watch. It was 5.15am. He frowned momentarily, then walked towards the door, slid back the bolt and opened it a fraction.

And there stood Bob the Milkie.

"Hullo, Gibby," he said with a broad grin on his face. He held up two pints of milk. "Here's twa pints o' Gold Top for yer last breakfast."

"I'm nae in Death Row or nithing," said Gibby crisply.

"Na, na," said Bob looking over Gibby's shoulder. "Bit I ken ye're awa til Edinburgh for a wikk and I thocht Flo wid like something special for yer send-off, so here I am wi twa pints o' Gold Top. Nae charge."

Gibby took the milk. "That's affa kind o' ye, Bob," he said. "And as lang as Gold Top's the only something special ye've got in mind, we hinna ony problems, you and me, hiv we?"

Bob looked blank, the grin frozen nervously on his face.

"So ye get ma drift?" said Gibby.

"Eh ... fairly that," said Bob.

"I'm richt pleased we understand een anither," said Gibby. "Richt pleased."

"Aye," said Bob. "Well, see and enjoy yersel in the big city and dinna dee onything I widna dee."

"I'll fairly enjoy masel in Edinburgh," said Gibby. "And see you dinna dee onything I think ye wid fairly dee if ye thocht ye'd get aff wi't. Now, cheerio and I'm sure we'll meet again fan I get back." And Gibby shut the door gently.

"Fa wis that at the door at this oor?" said Flo, shovelling spoonfuls of scrambled eggs into an impossibly engineered heap on the middle of Gibby's plate.

"A wellwisher wi a present for ma last breakfast," said Gibby, and he put the two bottles of Gold Top on to the kitchen table.

Flo flushed.

"Aye," said Gibby. "Bob. He's an enterprisin milkie, that. It disna maitter fit time o' day it is, Bob's the milkie that reaches bits ither milkies dinna reach. He fairly reaches my hackles, onywye. Snuffin aboot at five in the mornin noo. He surely thocht I left yesterday."

"Dinna be silly now, Gibby," said Flo. "Dinna spile yer last mornin here wi silliness. Bob's genuine enough. He thocht he wis bein kind. And, onywye, this is the middle o' the day for milkies. He jist hidna wintit ti miss ye so he could hand ower his present."

"Ach weel," said Gibby. "Bob and me fairly understand een anither noo. We jist cleared the air."

"Ye didna dee nithing silly?" said Flo. "Ye didna mak a scene on the doorstep at five in the mornin?"

"Nae scene," said Gibby. "Nae scene ata. Jist an explanation o' the position. I dinna think ye'll be bothered wi Bob again."

"He's nae a bother," said Flo. "He's the milkie."

"And as lang as he sticks ti bein the milkie, we've nae problems," said Gibby, sitting down to tackle the breakfast before him. "My, ye've fairly worked hard on this breakfast."

"If this is this jealousy again, Gibby," said Flo. "I'll ... well ... I'll ..."

"Nae jealousy," said Gibby calmly through a mouthful of sausage. "Jist clearin the air."

"Like I said," said Flo. "That jealousy'll land you in trouble ae day." And she glowered at Gibby as she walked over to switch on the kettle.

THE train pulled into Montrose Station and Gibby had barely noticed that they had left Aberdeen. He was preoccupied. Normally, his gaze would never have left the legs of the pretty young student in the miniskirt sitting on the other side of the aisle, but he stared blankly out of the window and thought of Flo, and the more he thought of Flo the more he wanted to be at home and not so many miles away studying gardening.

The more he thought of Flo, the more he thought of Bob. And the more he thought of Bob, the more he thought of Bob and Flo. And the more he thought of Bob and Flo, the more restless and riled he became.

When the woman pushing the snacks trolley shoogled his shoulder and asked if he would like anything, he replied: "A shotgun." The poor woman bustled off with her trolley and passengers round about stared at Gibby as though he were mad.

"I know their sandwiches are bad, chum," said a commercial traveller sitting opposite, "but murder ain't the answer." He grinned, as if waiting for a response. Gibby smiled emptily.

The train was pulling out of Montrose when Gibby muttered to himself. "Pull yersel thegither, Gibby. This is silliness. Flo's richt enough. He's got a face lik a horse's dowp. He's nae catch. She's got mair sense. She said hersel that jealousy wid get the better o' ye ae day. Dinna be silly."

But no amount of rationalising could set Gibby's mind at rest, and all the way to Edinburgh he dwelled on his wife and Bob the Milkie and what he would do to Bob if ever he found that anything improper had been going on behind his back.

"Stronach's ower sma a placie," said Gibby, as the train crawled past Burntisland.

"What's that, chum?" said the commercial traveller, and Gibby realised that he had spoken a little too loudly for privacy.

"Eh? Oh, nithing," said Gibby. "Sorry if I've disturbed ye."

"Worried about the wife at home?" said the traveller.

Gibby looked puzzled. "How did ye ken that?" he said. And the traveller slid his paper to one side and sat forward. "Chum," he said. "You've been muttering to yourself for the last hour and a half. I couldn't help hearing. Your wife and Bob the milkman. And if he ever lays a finger on her you're going to top him. Have I got the gist?"

Gibby flushed and stammered. The thought that he had been so careless with his private matters appalled him. "Eh... eh ..."

"C'mon, chum," said the traveller. "We're men of the world, you and me. Men of the world. Seen a lot. Done a lot. Regretted a lot, too, I don't wonder. Crikey, I'm hardly ever at home and I never worry for a minute about my wife. I trust her implicitly. If I didn't, I'd be a nervous wreck doing a job like this. All over the country. Never the same bed two nights running. Trust, my old chum. That's the secret. Trust." And he paused while the message sank in.

"First time away from home?" said the traveller.

Gibby nodded.

"It's natural," said the traveller. "Believe me, it's a lot easier if you put it out of your mind and trust her. Chances are you've nothing to worry about. Has she given you any cause for doubting her before now?"

Gibby shook his head.

"There you go, old man," said the traveller. "You're working yourself into knots for nothing at all. Put it to the back of your mind. Make the most of your time away. Work hard. Play hard. And buy her a bunch of flowers on your way home. It works wonders." And he winked a dirty wink.

Gibby smiled a little more easily.

"Ye really think so?" he said.

"I know so, me old mate," said the traveller. "You're listening to the voice of experience here. Eighteen years on the road and never a moment's worry. Never a single hint of anything improper. And we still get on like a house on fire. I bet it's the same for you. What line are you in, anyway?"

"I'm a gardener," said Gibby, and the traveller looked impressed and spent the next few minutes asking for advice on how to pep up a tired suburban garden, which took Gibby's mind off his worries. Before he knew it, the train was pulling into Waverley.

"I think this is where you get off, me old mate," said the traveller, and Gibby jumped up to drag his two suitcases out of the rack at the end of the carriage.

"Well, thanks a lot,' said Gibby. "Thanks for ... ye ken ... well ..."

"Think nothing of it, mate," said the traveller. "Thanks for the greenfinger advice. You'll make a gardener of me yet. And remember. Jealousy's a terrible thing. Eats you up if you let it. Lands you in all sorts of trouble for no reason at all. Don't let it do that to you."

Gibby smiled and stepped towards the carriage door.

"Oh, and chum," called the traveller, and Gibby stopped and looked back.

"If I'm wrong, you'll save a fortune in your milk bill."

And Gibby laughed.

GIBBY found his way to the college with few problems, although he thought the taxi fare a little steep. He was shown to his lodgings at the halls of residence, then made his way down to the enrolment hall, where he assembled with 40 other students from around Britain. He thought most of them looked too young to know anything about gardening, but he made polite conversation all the same.

The first day went in surprisingly quickly, although it concentrated a little too much on classroom work and theory for Gibby's liking. He'd have preferred being out and about getting soil beneath his fingernails.

It wasn't until he was back in his little room at 5.30pm that his mind began wandering from the events of a hectic day and back north to Stronach. And that old spectre of Bob and Flo began to haunt him as he lay on his uncomfortable and thin bed and stared at a dingy ceiling.

Flo.

Bob.

Flo and Bob.

He sighed and turned over.

Bob and Flo.

Flo and Bob.

He sat up and fluffed up the pillows, then put his hands behind his head and lay back to think. And all he could think of was Flo and Bob.

"This is silliness, Gibby," he heard himself muttering. "Jealousy's an affa thing. Trust. That's the secret. The traveller boy on the train said so. Trust's the secret. Jealousy eats ye up. Jealousy lands ye in trouble..."

He thought, propped up like that, for fully 20 minutes more before he swung his feet out over the edge, fumbled in his jacket pocket for small change and headed downstairs for the public phones.

"It'll be richt fine ti hear her," he said to himself as he dialled the number. "And Cassandra'll be excited hearin me fae far awa."

The phone rang for four or five rings then the receiver was lifted and he could hear fumbling at the other end. Then came the small voice of a very small young lady. And Gibby smiled.

"Hullo, darlin," he said, unable to stop himself grinning. "It's dad here. How are ye?"

"OK," she said, giggling.

"Are ye bein a good girl?"

"A good girl," she giggled.

"That's good," said Gibby. "Could I speak ti mummy?"

"OK." And the line went dead.

Gibby looked at the receiver. Then he grinned. "She's put doon the phone, bless her," he said.

He pushed another 50p into the slot, then dialled again.

"Hullo, darlin," he said when she answered the phone again. "Dinna pit doon the phone now. It's daddy here again. Could I speak ti mummy?"

"Mummy's nae here."

"Is she hingin oot washin?"

"No, she's up the stairs."

"Oh, well could ye go and get her?"

"No."

"Fit wye's that?"

"She's up the stairs with Uncle Bob."

Gibby felt the heat rising in his cheeks.

"Up the stairs wi Uncle Bob?"

"Aye." And there was another small-girl giggle from the other end of the line and a lot of loud fumbling and clattering with the receiver.

"Dinna pit doon the phone, dearie," urged Gibby. "Please, for ony sake, dinna pit doon the phone. Tell me, fa's Uncle Bob?"

"Uncle Bob that sometimes visits when you're nae here."

Gibby felt a white flash of heat run through him. He couldn't think. He felt a lump in his throat. He felt panicky. He wanted to run away from the phone. He wanted to shout down the phone so Flo could hear. Yet he was rooted to the spot and almost struck dumb.

"Am I gettin a present?" came the giggle from the other end.

"Eh? ... Oh, oh ... yes. A good present for a good little girl. Eh... tell me. Far aboot upstairs are Mummy and Uncle Bob?"

"In the bedroom."

Gibby clapped his hand over the mouthpiece. This was all his nightmares rolled into one and coming true. So much for homespun philosophy from commercial travellers. These blighters didn't know anything. He'd been right all along and how stupid he'd been. All that soft-soap and patter from Flo and Bob before he left... They were making him look a fool, and no mistake.

Gibby tried to think, but a million confused thoughts were rattling round in his brain. His eyes darted from side to side, then he hunched over the mouthpiece again and whispered this time.

"Wid ye dee something for daddy? Wid ye be a good girl and dee that?"

"OK."

"Wid ye go upstairs and knock on the bedroom door and say that ye've jist seen daddy comin aff the bus at the end o' the street? Wid ye dee that?"

"OK."

"And then wid ye come back and tell me fit happens?"

"OK."

"That's a good girl. Off ye go now, and dinna pit the phone doon. Just pit it on the table." And Gibby heard the dull, echoey rattle and clatter of a phone being laid down on the table, then the small sounds of small feet trotting across the room, out into the hall and up the stairs.

He shook his head in fury and panic and despair. "Ye're a mug," he wailed at himself. "The minute yer back's turned and the twa o' them, they're ... well ... it disna bear thinkin aboot. Yer ain wife. And the milkie. The *milkie*. What a state. Ye'll be the lachin-stock o' the village this time. A richt mug. Saft Gibby and the Randy Milkie. He felt like sobbing, but he was too furious to sob. He felt like shouting, but he was too sad to shout. He was a cauldron of emotions and he needed time to think.

Then he heard the sound of small feet coming down stairs and through the hall. Presently, the phone clattered and banged and a small voice said: "Hullo?"

"Hullo, dearie. Daddy's here. Did ye manage?"

"Aye," and she giggled again. "Ta-ta."

"No!" shouted Gibby. "No! No! Dinna pit doon the phone! Hullo? Are ye there? Dinna pit doon the phone!"

"OK."

"That's a good girl. Dinna pit doon the phone. Now, tell me. Did ye say fit I asked ye ti say?"

"Aye."

"And fit happened?"

"Well, I went intil the bedroom and Mummy and Uncle Bob were in the bed. Under the covers."

"Oh, Lord," wailed Gibby to himself. "In front o' her ain little quinie. Is there nae shame?" He tried to compose himself and then asked: "OK, dearie, and did ye say that ye'd seen daddy comin aff the bus?"

"Aye."

"And fit happened next?"

"Well, they got affa upset and mummy jumped up oot o' the bed ... and ... and she'd nearly nae claes on ... and ... and she ran aboot the bedroom lookin for her goon ... and ... and she put on her goon and she wis shoutin at Uncle Bob and she wis greetin ... and ... and she tripped on the cord o' her goon and she fell forward and she banged her heid on the edge o' the dressin-table ... and ... and there's blood on her heid and she's nae movin ... and ... and I'm scared, daddy! I'm affa scared!"

"Oh, Lord," sighed Gibby. "Dinna be scared, dearie. Dinna be scared. Tell me, fit aboot Uncle Bob?"

"Well ... well, Uncle Bob wis shoutin and greetin and he jumped oot o' the bed ... and ... and he'd nearly nae claes on ... and ... and he ran roon the bedroom shoutin and greetin ... and ... and then he opened the windi."

"And fit else?" said Gibby.

"Daddy, are you comin hame?"

"Yes, dearie, I'll be hame jist as soon as I can and I winna leave ye ever again."

"And I will get a present?"

"Ye'll fairly get a present. A great big present. The best present ye've ivver seen. Now, fit aboot Uncle Bob? The rat."

"Well, he wis shouting and greetin and he opened the windi."

"Yes, yes, and fit happened efter that?"

"Well, he put his legs oot o' the windi ... and ... and he climbed on til the drainpipe and he began slidin doon the drainpipe, bit it came loose fae the wa and it broke ... and ... and Uncle Bob fell aff and he landit in the swimmin-pool ... and ... and ... I think he's hurtit."

Gibby stopped. And he thought for a moment.

"Swimmin-pool?" he said.

"Yes, daddy."

"Did ye say swimmin-pool?"

"Yes."

"Uncle Bob fell aff the wa and intil the swimmin-pool?"

"Yes."

Gibby stopped, clapped his hand over the receiver and thought a dozen panicky thoughts in a flash. Then he took his hand away and spoke again:

"Hullo," he said.

"Yes?"

"Eh ... is that Stronach 263?"

Stronach Kitchen

Twelve tempting teas
to titillate
tired tastebuds

"I learned this recipe fae my grandmither, so ye ken how far back this goes. And it likely goes a lot farrer back nor that. I believe it wis a' the rage amon the fishers ben the Moray Firth fishin villagies lang afore the days o' timmer bilers.

I've jist put in a little suppie fish in this recipe. Well, fish is that pricey nooadays and I'm sure half o' it's stinkin lang afore it even sees yer kitchen. If ye're cookin for a femly, ye'd maybe better double the quantity.

A funny name, skink, isn't it? *Skink.* A cross atween skunk and stink, I aye think. Maybe that's the reason young folk need priggin wi afore they'll try it. Jist tell them it's a fish-stew soup. They'll lap it up.

I believe the real name comes fae Gaelic and it jist means "stew-soup". Ebenezer tells me there's a country version fae the sheep country ca'ed mutton skink — a mutton-stew soup. I think the blighter's haein me on.

Like a lotta aul things, this is comin back intil fashion nooadays. Maybe there's hope for me yet.

Mother Dreep's
CULLEN SKINK

(Serves 4)

Ingredients
A large smoked haddock (preferably Finnan)
   or
450g (1lb) fillet of haddock
Water to cover
Medium onion, chopped
500ml (1 pint) milk
50g (2oz) butter
225g (8oz) mashed potatoes
Salt and pepper
Chopped parsley to garnish
60ml (4 tbsp) single cream, optional

1. Place the fish, onion, pepper and water into a large pan and bring to the boil. Cover and simmer for 15 minutes.

2. Remove the fish and, when cool to touch, remove all the skin and bones.

3. Strain the stock and return it to the pan with the flaked fish, onion, milk, butter and potatoes.

4. Stir well. Bring back to the boil and simmer for a few minutes. Check to see if any salt and pepper are needed.

5. Serve garnished with the parsley and cream, if using.

" I likes a bowlie o' lentil soup on a caul winter's day, divn't you?

Ootside, folk's trumpin through slush and sna and puddles; there's blizzards fusslin aboot yer lum, and you're cosy at yer ain fireside wi a bowlie o' lentil soup. Roon yer hert lik a hairy worm. Fairly kittles ye up.

This soup recipe is an accident, really. Maist o' my cookin's an accident nooadays. I canna see the same, ye see.

Last winter, I thocht: 'Dosh,' I thocht. 'Awa and mak a panna lentil soup til yersel.' So awa ben til the kitchen I goes.

I wis cuttin up an ingin, only it turned oot it wisna an ingin. It wis a Grunny Smith's aeple. Bit, oh, what fine soup!

So I pits an aeple in a' ma soup nooadays. The sharper the aeple the better. I'd recommend cookers, bit a good, sharp Grunny Smith's fae Chile or South Africa or New Zealand is jist the dab. Dinna bother wi that French trock. Bugs o' watter.

Of course, nae a' my kitchen trugedies is as lucky as that. Atween you and me, I canna get affa excitit aboot Eve's Puddin made wi ingins.

Dorothy Birze's
LENTIL SOUP

(Serves 6)

Ingredients
225g (8oz) lentils
2 medium onions
1 small cooking apple
1 medium carrot
825ml (1½pints) ham or chicken stock
(You can also use a bacon rasher chopped up)
Salt and pepper
Chopped parsley

1. Put the lentils in a bowl and cover with water. Leave to soak for 2-4 hours.

2. Peel and chop the onions, carrot and apple finely. De-rind and chop up the bacon, if you're using bacon.

3. Drain the lentils and put in a large pan with the stock (and bacon), the apple, the vegetables and the salt and pepper.

4. Bring to a simmer for 1¼ to 1½ hours, until the lentils are soft.

5. Sieve or liquidise the soup. Check the seasoning, and heat thoroughly. Add chopped parsley before serving.

"Now, afore ye ask, this salmon is obtained by legitimate means. I dinna believe in haein onything ti dee wi poachers. Especially if the bobbies is watchin.

I dinna usually bother wi funcy cookin. I jist rip oot the intimmers, aff wi the heid and slap it in a pannie. Food fit for a king.

Onywye, the editor o' this book said I couldna jist pit doon:

1. Rip Oot Intimmers.
2. Aff Wi Heid.
3. Slap In Pan.

Nae funcy enough for him, appeerently. (Big nancy). So I thocht I'd maybe gie ye this recipe fae ma son and dother-in-law at their boardin-hoose at Portsoy. Believe me, there's plenty salmon knockin aboot at Portsoy.

I've tried it wi a' this lemon butter and weeds on it and it fairly maks a difference. I canna be bothered wi a ficher lik that masel, bit it fairly kittles up the taste. Ma dother-in-law says ye can use a hale wheen o' different weeds and fruit: Tarragon wi Limes, or Chives wi Oranges. Gad sakes.

Erchie Sotter's
GRILLED SALMON STEAKS
with Basil and Lemon Butter

(Serves 4)

Ingredients
Four 100-175g (4-6oz) salmon steaks
Juice and grated rind of one lemon
Tablespoon chopped basil, plus leaves for decoration
50g (2oz) butter, softened
Salt and pepper
Lemon slices for decoration

1. Add chopped basil, lemon juice and rind to the softened butter and mix thoroughly. Season to taste. Refrigerate for 30 minutes.

2. Pre-heat the grill on medium. Brush each salmon steak with oil and place them on the grill pan. Sprinkle with a little salt and pepper.

3. Grill on the lower level for three minutes. Turn them; brush with oil, and grill for another three minutes.

4. Place a knob of the basil-and-lemon butter on each steak and put them under the grill again until the butter just begins to melt.

5. Serve immediately, decorated with basil leaves and lemon slices.

❝This is one of those ordinary dishes made special with a little je-ne-sais-quoi (and a modicum of culinary skill and ingenuity, of course).

Fundamentally, it's a fairly standard chicken dish, but if you flame it with Calvados, that apple brandy from Normandy, it adds a certain piquancy and puts it in the cordon-bleu league.

People will swear they're eating something they remember vaguely from Le Gavroche, L'Ortolan, or from some other five-star restaurant — at least they do when they come to supper at Bridge House.

I always use red-skinned apples for colour contrast. Be careful not to overcook the apples so that they caramelise, otherwise it will be sickly sweet and terribly hard on the teeth.

One day, I'll use a green apple just for a bit of zip, perhaps with Cointreau instead of Calvados, but I'm not entirely sure how that will look as a piece of presentation. Presentation's so terribly important, I find, don't you? So few people pay it the attention it deserves. Especially hereabouts.

94

Kate Barrington-Graham's
NORMANDY CHICKEN

(Serves 4)

Ingredients
30ml (2 tbsp) cooking oil
40g (1½oz) butter
4 chicken supremes
6 eating apples
Salt and freshly ground black pepper
4 sprigs thyme plus four for garnish
300ml (½pint) dry cider
25g (1oz) demerara sugar
60ml (4 tbsp) Calvados
60ml (4 tbsp) double cream

Oven
180C 350F Gas 4

1. Heat the oil with 25g (1oz) of the butter in a large flameproof casserole.

2. Add the chicken supremes and fry over a moderate heat until golden brown on all sides.

3. Remove from the pan and keep warm.

4. Core and slice four apples in rings and fry them gently until they are lightly coloured.

5. Place the chicken pieces on top of the apple slices. Season with salt and pepper. Add the thyme and cider and bring to the boil. Cover and place in the oven for 45 minutes.

6. Prepare the two remaining apples as before and fry in the remaining butter with the sugar. Place them over the chicken.

7 Warm the Calvados gently in a ladle or small pan, then ignite it and add to the chicken. As soon as the flames have died down, garnish with thyme and trickle with cream.

6 6 Hello! And a very, very homely welcome to *all* of you. First of all — to begin with, as you might say — could I say how terribly super it is to have this chance to share one of our favourite recipes from the Manse. Super.

I'm sure most of you won't even have dreamed of eating a nut roast, let alone making one, but it's really so terribly simple. There's nothing easier. I leave it all to my wife. You can't get much easier than that now, can you? Ha-ha. Just my little joke.

Seriously, just whizz together all the nuts and things. If you don't want a loaf, you can shape it into burgers and fry them for four minutes each side, which is good for kiddies' parties.

The loaf will look terribly wizened and dry when it comes out of the oven but, trust me (and isn't trust the key to everything, after all?), when you slice it open, it'll be moist and aromatic and just oh so yummy.

My wife makes this for me only when I'm spending a day in the garden — and, funnily enough, only when the wind is blowing East, I've noticed. Hmm.

Rev Montgomery Thole's
NUT ROAST

(Serves 4)

Ingredients
1 tbsp sunflower oil
1 onion, chopped finely
225g (8oz) mixed nuts
100g (4oz) brown bread
1 tsp dried thyme *or* 2 tsps fresh thyme
2 tbsps chopped parsley
Black pepper and salt to taste
1 egg made up to 150ml (5 fl oz) with vegetable stock

Oven
180C 350F Gas 4

1. Heat the oil in a frying pan and soften the onion.

2. In a liquidiser, food-processor, nut mill or coffee-grinder, grind the bread and the nuts until reasonably fine.

3. Transfer the contents into a bowl and add the onion, herbs and seasoning, mixing well.

4. Stir in the egg mixture until incorporated evenly.

5. Line a 450g (1lb) loaf tin with foil. Grease it with oil and add the mixture. Press it down well and make sure it is level.

6. Put the dish on a baking tray and cook for 40 minutes, until firm.

7. Cool slightly before turning out and slicing.

❝Frankly, I canna see ony need for recipes for skirlie or doughballs. Ony housewife that canna mak skirlie or doughballs athoot a cookery book should be black affrontit.

You young lassies wi yer make-up and yer pizzas and yer convenience meals fae Marks and Spencer's — a dampt disgrace.

So here's a bit o' wir heritage for ye. Ye'll get a rare, warmin plate o' skirlie oot o' this. I've heard folk ask if there's a rule for tellin fan a pan o' skirlie's ready. Ye'll ken it's ready if it stots doon yer throat in loups and clatters. If it slides doon easy, it's ower thin.

Mind and cook the ingins till they're birstled. That'll gaur yer eenies watter. Skirlie's fine wi mince, bit I like it wi tatties, peas and a cup o' milk. Jist nectar.

Doughballs is oota fashion nooadays. They're nae affa healthy, I suppose, bit they fairly eke oot a pan o' mince. I like a stalk o' parsley through mine.

Dinna be ambitious and try aetin doughballs and skirlie at the same sittin. Ye'll be flat on yer back till Christmas.

Babbie Girn's
SKIRLIE

(Serves 4)

Ingredients

50g (2oz) shredded suet or dripping *or*
75g (3oz) margarine
2 medium onions, chopped finely
100g (4oz) medium oatmeal
Salt and pepper

1. Heat the suet or fat or margarine in a large frying pan
2. Add the onions, frying them until soft and brown.
3. Add the oatmeal, stirring well until it is well cooked (about five minutes).
4. Add the salt and pepper and stir well.

or DOUGHBALLS

(Serves 4)

Ingredients

100g (4oz) self-raising flour
Pinch of salt
Black pepper
50g (2oz) suet *or* low fat margarine
3 good-sized sprigs of parsley leaves, chopped finely

1. Sift the flour into a bowl and add the seasoning.
2. Stir in the suet or rub in the margarine and add parsley. Stir in just enough cold water to make a workable mixture.
3. Put flour on your fingers and form the dough into balls about the size of marbles. There should be about 16-20.
4. Drop them into the mince about 15 minutes before serving. Test one by cutting it open to be sure it has cooked through.

66 If I'm ever needin a favour fae Gibby, or if Wayne's been behavin himsel, I mak this puddin as a bribe, or a reward. Their little eenies licht up like Christmas trees. I'm partial til it masel, in fact.

We were richt lucky gettin a photie o' it, for it usually vanishes as quick as it's oot o' the kitchen. Gibby's lugs hinna stopped stingin yet.

Banoffi's affa fillin, though, so I warn ye, dinna mak the helpins ower big. Even if ye think ye've a sweet tooth and ye'll easy cope, ye'll fooner lang afore yer platie's teem. A little Banoffi goes a lang, lang wye.

Ye can mak it a bittie less fillin if ye slice a twa-three bananas ower the fillin afore ye clart on the cream. Then pit a pucklie bananas on top o' the cream.

If ye're layin on the top bananas a whilie afore ye're servin, mind an dip the banana slices in lemon juice or lime juice. If ye dinna, the bananas'll turn black and it winna look affa appetisin, though black bananas hisna stopped Gibby or Wayne in the past.

100

Flo Spurtle's
BANOFFI PIE

(Serves 4-6)

Ingredients
Base:
20cm (8in) baked shortcrust pastry base
or use the biscuit-base recipe on Page 103

Filling:
397g (14 oz) tin condensed milk
100g (4oz) butter
100g (4oz) caster sugar

Topping:
2 ripe bananas
Lemon or lime juice
Fine strips of lemon or lime rind *or* grated chocolate
for decoration
150ml ($\frac{1}{4}$ pint) carton of whipping or double cream

1. Pour the condensed milk into a non-stick pan and add the butter and sugar.
2. Stir over a low heat until the sugar dissolves, then boil for five minutes, stirring all the time, until a pale caramel colour.
3. Pour into the base and leave to cool.
4. Slice the bananas and dip the slices in the lemon or lime juice. Arrange them over the top of the pie.
5. Whip the cream and cover the pie, adding the decoration of your choice.

❝This recipe startit as an experiment and it became the best poodin in my repertoire. I'd got an affa big crop o' reidcurrants aff ma bushes at the fit o' the gairden ae year.

Well, fin ye've made a twa-three dizzen jars o' jam and jeely, fit else is there? Nae much, that's fit. Nae an affa versatile fruit, the reidcurrant, is it?

So I thocht a poodin wid be a fine change. And here it is. I win prizes wi this poodin. Big prizes. Three steen o' tatties. A year's supply o' oatmeal. Things like that.

The surprise wi this poodin is the snappiness o' the toppin. It's licht and fluffy, bit it's got a bit o' a tartiness aboot it, tee. Dinna ficher aboot wi the toppin, bit ye can experiment wi the base. I sometimes use ginger snaps instead o' digestives. Sometimes I add twa ounces o' sugar til the biscuits for a crunchiness.

If I'm feelin really devil-may-care, I use Fox's chocolate-ginger biscuits. What a Rolls-Royce poodin ye get. Nae cheap, bit it's worth it for special occasions. Ye can even use berries fae the freezer. An affa fine surprise at Christmas.

Virginia Huffie's
REDCURRANT GOSSAMER PIE

(Serves 6)

Ingredients

225g (8oz) digestive biscuits, crumbed
100g (4oz) butter, melted
450g (1lb) redcurrants
2 eggs, separated
75g (3oz) caster sugar
2 level tsps gelatine
1 tbsp water

1. Make the base by combining the biscuit crumbs with the butter. Press the mixture into a 9in pie plate. Chill in the fridge.

2. Stew the redcurrants and sieve them.

3. Whisk the egg yolks and caster sugar in a Pyrex bowl until pale in colour, then add the redcurrant puree.

4. Place this bowl of mixture over a pan of hot water and whisk until thick.

5. Dissolve the gelatine in the water, then whisk it into the mixture until it is on the point of settting.

6. Whisk the egg whites until stiff and then fold carefully into the mixture.

7. Pile the mixture on to the biscuit base and chill well.

“ “I'm nae much o' a cookin haun masel, bit I fairly like this. It disna tak much effort, bit what a golden glow ye get for a twa-three oors efterhin.

Ye're also helpin keep alive the Scottish heritage, because this is as near as ye'll get til a Scottish national poodin now that the English his hijacked trifle. Bliddy thieves. As if they hinna enough poodins o' their ain. They pinch oor poodins and pass them aff as English. (They've aye been the dampt same).

Onywye, fresh rasps is best if it's the season, bit frozen rasps is nearly as good and a lot handier through the year. Mind and let them thaw oot afore ye start. Ye dinna wint them thawin in the bowlies and waterin doon the cream (or the whisky!).

I've tried speedin up this recipe by deein athoot the toastit oatmeal, or by nae botherin toastin it. Believe me, it disna work. Toastin oatmeal's a bit o' a footer, bit ye hinna got the genuine Cranachan if ye dinna, ye see. And ye can aye hae anither dram the time ye're waitin.

104

Ebenezer Grip's
CRANACHAN

(Serves 6)

Ingredients

75g (3oz) oatmeal, toasted and cooled
275ml (½ pint) double cream
50g (2oz) caster sugar
50ml (2 fl oz) malt whisky *(I prefer The Macallan)*
225g (8oz) raspberries

1. Whip the cream and add the sugar and whisky slowly, while whipping. Stop when the mixture is standing in soft peaks.
2. Spoon raspberries into serving glasses.
3. Add a layer of cream.
4. Finish off with a sprinkle of toasted oatmeal.

"Is the wifie Dreep listenin? No? I'm sweir ti gie ye this recipe, for this is the finest poodin oot and that aul craw'll jist claim it wis hers first. She's like that.

Ye winna believe how creamy this chocolate toppin is. If ye're a chocoholic, this is the poodin for you. Really decadent and dead simple. It's a bittie like a good episode o' Tak the High Road. Ye dinna wint it ti stop.

Bakin the base first maks it firmer and it helps the chocolate melt and stick. Wi a poodin lik this, ye dinna wint yer run-o'-the-mill cheesecake base crumblin a' ower the place.

Try and whip the cream til the same consistency as the chocolate mixture afore ye fold it in. If ye're really in a hurry, I suppose ye can pit the cream in the food-processor and whip it there, bit I aye think ye're jist makkin washin-up for yersel wi a food-processor. Also, I hinna got een.

Dinna cut corners foldin in the egg whites. That's the secret. Be slow and patient. Tak yer time. It's worth it in the end. Believe me.

Now, far's that wifie Dreep? His she been luggin in?

106

Geneva Brose's
SINFUL CHOCOLATE CREAM PIE

Biscuit base

10 dark-chocolate wholemeal biscuits, crushed finely

75g (3oz) butter, melted

Filling

175g (6oz) dark chocolate (Terry's or Bournville)

225g (8oz) cream cheese

100g (4oz) caster sugar

1 tsp vanilla essence

2 eggs, separated

150ml (¼ pint) of double cream

Oven

180C 350F Gas 4

1. Mix the crumbs and melted butter together and press round the sides and bottom of a flan dish measuring 8 or 10in diameter. Bake for 15 minutes.

2. Remove from the oven and cool.

3. Put the chocolate in a Pyrex bowl and melt the chocolate gently over a pan of hot water. A microwave oven at low power is even easier.

4. Put the cream cheese, caster sugar, vanilla essence into a food-processor and whizz until smooth. (If you don't have a processor, a mixing bowl and wooden spoon are OK).

5. Whizz or beat the egg yolks into the mixture one by one.

6. Whizz or beat in the cooled, melted chocolate.

7. If you have been using a food-processor, now transfer the mixture into a large mixing bowl.

8. Whip the cream and fold it into the chocolate mixture.

9. Whisk egg whites until they are stiff. Fold in using a metal spoon.

10. Put the mixture into the cold biscuit base and leave to set.

Will freeze successfully.   Maximum storage six months

"Is the wifie Brose listenin? No? I'm sweir to gie ye this recipe, for this is the finest cakie oot and that aul craw'll jist claim it wis hers first. She's like that.

There's nae really a great secret til this cake. There's nae a secret ingredient or a special technique that guarantees success. It's jist a richt fine cake. Tasty. Moist. Licht as fit's inside Gibby Spurtle's heid.

There's an almondy flavour aboot it fae the almond essence. Ye can manage athoot the essence, I suppose, if ye're nae affa fond o' nutty tastes, bit ye'll spile the cakie, if ye ask me.

Fin ye're siftin in the flooer, mind and haud the sieve real high ower the bowl. Let the flooer fa fae a great hicht. Get the air in aboot it. That's a must for a really licht cake.

Under no circumstances mak this cake if ye're on a diet or thinkin aboot a diet. Ye'll pit on the beef jist lookin at this cakie. Ye tak a slice and ye think ye'll hae the willpower ti stop at jist the one. Bit ye winna. And yer weicht'll jist zoom.

On second thochts, maybe the wifie Brose *should* be telt aboot it.

Aggie Dreep's
PARADISE CAKE

Ingredients

225g (8oz) butter or margarine

225g (8oz) caster sugar

4 large eggs, beaten

$\frac{1}{2}$ tsp almond essence

275g (10oz) self-raising flour

110g (4oz) mixed dried fruit

50g (2oz) flaked almonds

50g (2oz) glace cherries

$1\frac{1}{2}$ tbsps granulated sugar

Oven

180C   350F   Gas 4

1. Grease a tin measuring 10x8in (25x20cm) and 2in (5cm) deep.

2. Cream the butter and caster sugar until pale and fluffy, then add the eggs gradually, beating well after each addition.

3. Add the almond essence and beat once more.

4. Fold in the sifted flour carefully, a little at a time.

5. Fold in the dried fruit and cherries.

6. Transfer the mixture into the prepared tin, spreading it evenly.

7. Sprinkle the surface with the granulated sugar and the flaked almonds.

8. Bake in the middle of the oven for 45-55 minutes, until the centre feels springy.

9. Leave to cool in the tin for 10 minutes before turning out.

" THIS is anither recipe fae the Wayne Spurtle school o' makkin a richt soss in yer mither's kitchen. The great thing aboot this recipe is the fun ye can hae bashin the biscuits. Bash, bash, bash. It gets a' the frustration o' bein a kid oot o' yer system and it saves wear and tear on yer little sister's lugs.

My pal, Puddick, and me sometimes mak this on a rainy day. We get a lotta rainy days at Stronach, so we get a lotta pieces made. We get a lotta pieces eaten, as weel.

The editor o' this bit o' the book says we should include tips and shortcuts ti help folk lik you along, this bein the first time ye've maybe tried a recipe lik this.

So Puddick says dinna bash the biscuits ower fine. Leave a pucklie crunchy bits so the base his an interestin texture. Ye dinna wint it turnin oot slabby.

And my tip is: hae a bucket handy. Ye'll eat a lotta this biscuits and yer mither winna like it if ye spew on her carpet.

110

Wayne Spurtle's
CHOCOLATE GOODIES

Ingredients

225g (8 oz) digestive biscuits

50g (2oz) caster sugar

2 tbsps golden syrup

110g (4oz) butter or margarine

3 level tbsps cocoa

1tsp vanilla essence

Topping

175g (6oz) icing sugar

50g (2oz) cocoa

2 drops vanilla essence

A little boiling water

1. Grease a 10x8 (25x20cm) swiss-roll tin.

2. Put the biscuits inside a polythene bag and bash them with a rolling pin until they are almost crumbs. (Or you can put them in a food processor).

3. Put the sugar, syrup and butter into a pan and melt over a low heat. Bring to the boil. Remove from the heat and stir in the cocoa and vanilla essence. Stir in the biscuit crumbs until all the liquid is absorbed, then spread the mixture evenly into the tin, pressing it down well.

4. Now make the topping by sieving the icing sugar and the cocoa into a bowl.

5. Add the vanilla essence and spoonfuls of boiling water until you have a spreading consistency, beating it well after each addition.

6. Spread the topping over the base.

7. Cut the slab into squares once it has set.

Glossary

A gentleman's guide to Stronachese

Let it serve for table-talk;
Then, howsoe'er thou speaks't, 'mong other things,
I shall digest it.

— W. Shakespeare
The Merchant of Venice, 1596

The accent of one's birthplace lingers in the mind
and in the heart, as it does in one's speech.

— F. Rochefoucauld
Les Maximes, 1671

I'm nae carin if it's language, dialect, accent or fit the
hell it is. It's jist the wye I spik.

— B. Girn
Outside post office after collecting pension, 1993

Acquant: *Familiar*
Ebenezer Grip is acquant with everyone in the Howe of Stronach

Aeples: *Apples*
There's nothing tastier than aeples, especially from someone else's tree

Aetin: *Eating*
One of life's challenges is aetin raspberry jam with false teeth

Affrontit, black: *Ashamed, embarrassed*
Anyone who doesn't make the beds before lunchtime should be black affrontit

Aneth: *Beneath, below*
Kate Barrington-Graham thinks socialising in the village is aneth her

Athoot: *Without*
A smile is not a smile athoot your top plate

Aye aye, min: *Hullo there, good fellow*
"Aye aye, min. Haven't seen you in ages. Are you keeping well?"

Been: *(n.) Bone*
When Floretta had mild anorexia, she was nothing but skin and been

Ben: *Through*
The Dreeps eat in the kitchen, while Mother Dreep dines ben in her bedroom

Bide: *Stay (usu. place of residence)*
Babbie Girn bides next door to Virginia Huffie

Birstled: *Burned, sizzled*
Sandy prefers his Sunday-morning sausages birstled black

Bitta stuff: *Young female companion (aka The Blonde, The Dame)*
If my bitta stuff's skirt was any shorter, she'd have two more cheeks to powder

Bosie: *Embrace, hug, cuddle*
Cassandra burst into tears. Only a bosie from her mum made it better

Choobs: *(anat.) Intestines or sundry offal*
Sandy Brose has terrible problems with his choobs, thanks to his unhealthy diet

Claik: *Gossip*
Contrary to stereotype, men are far worse claiks than women

Clappit: *Clapped, patted*
Geneva choked on a fishbone. Sandy clappit her back while Aggie laughed

Clart: *Slap on to excess (v.)*
Floretta clarts on the make-up before a night out on the town

Clart: *Farmyard manure, slurry (n.)*
Even the cleanest farmyard is tainted to some degree with clart

Clart, dropped in: *Laid open to harassment, trouble or ridicule*
When you feel things can't get worse, someone is bound to drop you in the clart

Clart, thick as: *Of limited intelligence*
Sandy insists it is an advantage to be as thick as clart to stand for the council

Clatter: *Rattle (usu. tinny) (onom.)*
Geneva's corsets clatter in the breeze when the wind is in the north

Cockachesscoo: *Romanian dictator Nicolae Ceausesçu (dec.)*
That chap Cockachesscoo had a novel style of government

Contermacious: *Awkward, deliberately difficult*
There's no point discussing it; Aggie's in one of her contermacious moods

Coorse: *Bad, coarse*
As farmers, especially, know, there's nothing as coorse as cat's dirt

Coup: *Tip, topple, empty out*
Erchie Sotter feels that to coup a glass of whisky is to commit a capital offence

Craiters: *Creatures (usu. derog)*
They're poor craiters, ministers. Free houses and work one day a week

Crochlie: *Infirm, unsure of step*
Dorothy Birze has twisted her ankle. She's feeling rather crochlie

Deein athoot: *Forgoing*
When you're short of cash, you must think of deein athoot life's little luxuries

Dockens: *Dock leaves, a tenacious weed*
Dockens: Nature's environmentally friendly alternative to Andrex

Dominie: *Headmaster (usu. male)*
Sammy always wanted to be a dominie, but decided he couldn't take the stress

Doon aboot the mou: *Depressed, out of sorts*
Ebenezer has been doon aboot the mou since he gave 1p too much in change

Dother: *Daughter*
Floretta Brose is Geneva and Sandy's dother, although she bears the burden well

Dowp: *(anat.) Backside, posterior*
Sandy told Geneva she had a hippo's dowp. His condition is said to be stable

Dyeucks: *Ducks*
There's nothing quite so filling as a roast dyeuck, unless it's *two* roast dyeucks

Eenies: *Eyes (dimin.)*
Invited into Mrs Barrington-Graham's home, Aggie's eenies were everywhere

Efterhin: *Afterwards*
Erchie enjoys a rasp-jam sandwich, and always sucks his dentures efterhin

Ficher: *Fiddle, interfere (v.)*
Aggie Dreep is notorious for fichering in other people's private affairs

Fit's worst wi ye?: *How are you?*
Standard North-east greeting, familiar to students of the French form: "Ça va?"

Flechy: *Infested with parasites*
The 1903 mink stole worn by Mother Dreep is threadbare and flechy

Footer: *Fiddle, nuisance, waste of time*
Gibby would achieve much more if he spent less time footering

Forrit: *Forward*
Floretta failed her driving test when she engaged reverse and went forrit

Fusslin: *Whistling*
A golf ball went fusslin past Gibby's ears at the Stronach Golf Course

Futret: *Weasel or stoat (**not** a ferret). Now usually derogatory*
As an example of the futret genre, Wayne has no equal, according to Babbie Girn

Gad sakes!: *Yeuch! (exclam.)*
This is not entirely to my taste

Gadgie: *Chap, fellow*
Saddam Hussein; what a gadgie for telling fibs

Ganzie: *Sweater, cardigan*
Dorothy is sporting a fetching new ganzie in purple and orange stripes

Gaur: *Make*
The smell of a new pot of broth fairly gaurs yer teeth watter

Gey: *Quite, really*
Sandy was gey wobbly after his Thursday-evening sojourn at the Stronach Arms

Gulshich: *Sweetmeats*
Wayne Spurtle wastes his pocket money on crisps, Mars Bars and other gulshich

Gype: *Idiot, poltroon (usu. male)*
Were it not for Gibby's gardening skills, he would be a complete gype

Hale: *Whole*
Virginia's limit is half a softie and syrup, but Babbie can manage a hale one

Hallyrackit: *Uncouth, raw (usu. young woman)*
Babbie was hallyrackit in her day, and has scarcely calmed down now

Hinder end: *End (taut.) pron. "hinner"*
Erchie Sotter is usually at the hinder end when it comes to standing his hand

Hirply: *Hobbly, unsteady*
Erchie's hirply gait is due not to the infirmity of age, but the alcohol of decades

Ilky: *Each*
Ilky time Erchie mixes his drinks, he ends up on his back. You'd think he'd learn

Ill-natered: *Not of sunny disposition (usu. married female)*
Geneva is at her most ill-natered when in the vicinity of Aggie Dreep

Ingin: *Onion*
The ingin is an essential ingredient for really good mince

Intimmers: *(anat.) Insides*
Erchie's hobby is exploring the intimmers of clocks, watches and bottles of malt

Ivnoo: *Now, at this moment*
I would shake your hand, but I find myself somewhat fouled with dog dirt ivnoo

Jinkin: *Ducking and diving, chicaning*
Wayne would receive many more parental skelps were it not for his skill at jinkin

Jints: *(anat.) Joints*
Walter's jints have suffered due to inferior-quality washing-up liquid

Jube-jube: *Small sweetmeat of sugar and jelly (usu. juvenile bribery)*
Wayne is promised a packet of jube-jubes if he is a good boy

Kirn-up: *Mess*
Wayne likes eating skirlie and custard on the same plate. What a kirn-up

Kittle up: *Enliven, invigorate*
Sammy thought he would kittle up Floretta in the back seat at the cinema

Knapdarlich: *Matted dung, hardened on an animal's backside*
Aggie's new hairdo looks like a knapdarlich hat

Loon: *Boy*
As loons go, Wayne Spurtle is one of the more behaviourally challenged

Losh be here!: *(exclam.) My goodness!*
Erchie got a strippagram for his birthday. All he could say was: "Losh be here!"

Loup: *Jump*
When charged by the bull, Gibby had two options: stand still or loup the fence

Mairriet: *Wed, married, betrothed*
Aggie and Walter revelled in each other's company. Then they got mairriet...

Mochey: *Grey, drab, dreary*
After 40 days and 40 nights, Noah said: "That wis most affa mochey weather."

Muggie: *Margaret (usu. Lady Thatcher)*
Say what you like about Muggie, but she never stood for any nonsense

Neuk: *Corner*
Erchie Sotter has his special neuk at the bar at the Stronach Arms

News: *(n.) Chat, discussion*
Dorothy says a news in the surgery waiting-room takes your mind off your ills

Nickum: *Imp, mischief-maker*
Wayne was a nickum to squirt shaving-foam in the toes of his mother's slippers

Oots and ins: *Kirby grips, hairpins*
Virginia buys a new packet of oots and ins every four weeks

Ower the heid: *A surfeit, in excess*
Erchie Sotter's garden is ower the heid with dockens, nettles and empty bottles

Pints: *Laces*
Virginia always thinks that brown pints and black shoes don't go well together

Plooky: *Pock-marked, enjoying a surfeit of pimples*
Sammy's formative years were marred by a somewhat plooky adolescence

Poodin: *Best part of any meal*
Trifle, Cranachan and Blaeberries with Cream: classic examples of Scots poodins

Pregment: *With child, expecting*
Floretta's parents thought she was pregment and they were somewhat dischuffed

Priggin wi: *Pleading with*

Priggin wi Wayne is the only way to get him to keep his bedroom tidy

Pucklie: *Small amount of*

Virginia likes throwing a pucklie rose petals when she attends a wedding

Pyokie: *Small bag containing something*

Babbie likes a pyokie of pandrops while she reads her People's Friend

Quaet: *Quiet, peaceful*

The Broses' bedroom is as quaet as a morgue on a Monday morning

Quine: *Girl*

Babbie longs for the days when she was a young quine, but those days are gone

Rake: *(n.) Exploration (usu. shopping, **not** hortic.)*

There's nothing like a rake at E&M's sale to cheer up a body

Riggit: *Ready (usu. sartorial)*

Dorothy got riggit for the pensioner's outing but forgot it had been cancelled

Rikkin: *Smoking, steaming*

The pile of farmyard manure was rikkin in the still of the autumn morning

Rive: *Rip, tear or wrench*

Erchie rived another piece of bread from the loaf. He couldn't find the breadknife

Roose: *To anger, inflame*

Nothing is more certain to roose Aggie than the mention of Geneva Brose's name

Rowin: *Wrapping*

Walter's least-favourite job is rowin up Christmas presents

Sair: *Sore, painful*

Kate Barrington-Graham; a richt sair erse

Sair-made: *Troubled, in pain*

Aggie was sair-made as she traversed the menopause

Scuddlin: *Idling, lazing (usu. while sartorially challenged)*

Now that Gibby has a full-time job, he misses scuddlin about at home

Sharn: *Slurry (usu. agricultural)*

The wafting aroma of ripe sharn announces the proximity of Wester Boggiedubs

Shooed: *Sewed, sewn*

Sandy wishes a public-spirited surgeon had shooed Geneva's lips together in 1958

Sikkin: *Needing, requiring*
Insurance salesmen hate visiting Stronach, for no one is sikkin them

Siller: *Money, cash*
Life would be a bed of roses for the Spurtles, but for a protracted lack of siller

Skirlie: *North-east delicacy, best with onions slightly burned*
Skirlie, peas, mashed tatties and a cup of milk — a meal fit for a king (See P99)

Skite: *Slide*
Winters on the Hill of Stronach are so bad that even tractors can skite off the road

Slubber: *To slurp (onom.)*
Deprived of his false teeth, Erchie had to slubber at his plate of broth

Sookit-lookin: *Puckered, wrinkled (usu. corpses or accountants)*
Ebenezer Grip turns sookit-lookin every time he has to pay a bill

Soss: *Mess*
Whenever Wayne tries his hand at cooking, he makes a soss of the kitchen

Spad: *Spade*
Babbie's nephew has a fine council job. He's the one that leans on the spad

Spew: *Vomit*
A look inside Erchie Sotter's fridge would make a saint spew

Spile: *Spoil, damage*
Floretta wears too much mascara and spiles a bonnie face

Spunks: *Matches, lucifers*
It is cheaper to utilise a disposable lighter than it is to purchase a box of spunks

Stots: *Bounces*
Wayne's favourite game is when he stots his ba against the dominie's door

Styter: *Stumble, stagger*
Erchie's step is steady when he's drunk. It's when he's sober that he styters

Sup: *Small amount (usu. liquid)*
There's nothing like a sup broth on a cold winter's night

Sweir: *Reluctant (adj.)*
Sammy was clearly in the mood for romance, but Floretta was sweir to comply

Sweir: *Swear (v.)*
Virginia sweirs that Babbie was a beauty in her day (August 22, 1941)

Teem: *Empty*

The sign of a hearty meal: full belly and teem plate

Tekkie: *Outing, trip, visit*

Babbie needed cheering up so she had a tekkie to the cemetery to see the wreaths

Timmer bilers: *Clothes-boilers made of wood (usu. euph. for days of old)*

The contents of Dorothy's wardrobe are from the days of timmer bilers

Toonsers: *Indigenes of Aberdeen (derog.)*

Wayne is so mischievous, he might be a Toonser's bairn

Trock: *Rubbish, debris, garbage (usu. concrete n., not abstract)*

The last Stronach bring-and-buy sale wasn't worth a visit. Just a lot of old trock.

Trumpin: *Tramping*

The worst aspect of a hard winter is trumpin through snowdrifts

Twa pun: *Two pounds (avoirdup.)*

If Gibby's brain weighs twa pun, it's a miracle

Tyauve: *Struggle (pron. "chaav")*

Walters tyauves with the ironing, and swears by tins of Co-opie starch

Waur nor: *Worse than*

To mock a Rangers supporter is no waur nor laughing at a Celtic fan

Wheen: *Good few*

There are a wheen o' rabbits up on top of the Hill of Stronach

Wheepit: *Whipped*

Walter proposed to Aggie after she wheepit him with her slippers one starry night

Wrang spy: *Mistaken identity*

The hedgehog climbed on to the lavvie-brush. A classic instance of wrang spy

Wyte: *Fault*

It wasn't Wayne's wyte that he was caught putting clingfilm over the school WC

Yestreen: *Previous evening*

Erchie's best hangover lasted from yestreen to this evening

Yokie: *Itchy*

Cassandra refuses to wear her new jersey; the mohair makes her feel yokie

Yowl: *Wail, whine*

When Walter stood on Huggis's tail, the little cattie let out a plaintive yowl

Stronach Mastermind

Here's your chance to put your Stronach knowledge to good use and win yourself some siller.

1. Answer the 12 multiple-choice questions on the next two pages.

2. Write your answers on a sheet of paper, remembering to add your name and address, and a daytime telephone number, if possible.

3. Attach the entry token on Page 127.

4. The first all-correct (or nearest all-correct) entry drawn after the closing date will win £50. The next two will win £25 each. The next two will win a complete set of Stronach books and tapes. Full rules are on Page 126.

Stronach

1. Which Stronach resident is a fully paid-up member of the Campaign to Protect Rural England?
    A. Babbie Girn.
    B. Euphemia Pink.
    C. Kate Barrington-Graham.

2. What is the name of the eventide home at Stronach?
    A. Crochlie Neuk.
    B. Bide-a-whilie.
    C. The Golden Staircase.

3. In 1992, Babbie Girn sold a piece of 16th-century Montibello porcelain for £80,000. She had been using it as a ... what?
    A. Bowl for hyacinth bulbs.
    B. Po.
    C. Tattie-pot.

4. Which Stronach pensioner's hobby is to sit in the waiting-room at the doctor's surgery and inquire after people's "choobs"?
    A. Virginia Huffie.
    B. Dorothy Birze.
    C. Erchie Sotter.

5. Erchie Sotter worked from 1946 to 1965 as ... what?
    A. Warehouseman at the Stronach Distillery.
    B. Engine driver and shunter on the Stronach branch railway line.
    C. Village street-sweeper.

6. Which Stronach couple met while they worked for Alexander's buses — he as a driver and she as a conductress?
    A. Flo and Gibby Spurtle.
    B. Geneva and Sandy Brose.
    C. Aggie and Walter Dreep.

Mastermind

7. Meggie Bachle, a crofter up on the Hill of Stronach, has only one visible means of support. How does she make her money?
    A. Take-away skirlie for holidaymakers.
    B. Oil paintings of Stronach scenes.
    C. Sells fresh eggs to shops.

8. What are the names of Flo and Gibby Spurtle's two children?
    A. Wayne and Cassandra.
    B. Wayne and Sharon.
    C. Wayne and Kylie.

9. Which famous Irish country-and-western star did a concert at the village hall in aid of the Stronach Pensioners Club?
    A. Patrick O'Clarty.
    B. Val Doonican.
    C. Paddy McGinty's goat.

10. Erchie Sotter's spends virtually every evening at the Stronach Arms. What is his favourite drink?
    A. Babycham.
    B. Herbal Tea.
    C. A good Speyside malt.

11. What is the full title of Ebenezer Grip's village shop?
    A. Stronach Emporium and General Stores.
    B. Stronach Grocery and Food Hall.
    C. Stronach General Merchant and Haberdashery.

12. When did dispatches from Stronach begin appearing in the Press and Journal every Saturday?
    A. 1984.
    B. 1987.
    C. 1989.

Stronach Mastermind
Rules

1. Employees of Stronach Media Ltd., their families and anyone else connected with the promotion of this competition are ineligible for entry.

2. Entry instructions form part of the rules.

3. No cash alternatives are available to winners of the runner-up prizes.

4. No correspondence can be entered into regarding the allocation of prizes.

5. Stronach Media Ltd. reserves the right to reject entries which are not accompanied by an original entry token.

6. Photocopies of entry tokens are not acceptable.

7. The closing date of the competition is January 31, 1994.

8. Entry is open to all readers, irrespective of country of domicile.

9. Prizes will be dispatched within 28 days.

10. Proof of posting will not be accepted as proof of delivery.

11. Entries lost, delayed, illegible or insufficiently stamped will be disqualified.

12. A list of winners will be available either by enclosing an SAE with your entry, or by sending an SAE to Stronach Media Ltd.after January 31, 1994.

Send your entries to:

Stronach Media Ltd., Tullynessle, Alford, Aberdeenshire, Scotland, AB33 8QN.

And good luck...

That's it for another year. We hope you've enjoyed this short stay in the village of Stronach and that you have found something to amuse you, inform you or just fatten you up.

You can keep up with all the villagers' adventures every Saturday morning in the Press and Journal. And remember, that The Stronach Tapes, with many of the stories from Volumes One and Two, as well as one or two others, are available on double cassette at all good bookshops and newsagents. Or you can order by post from the address below.

Stronach: Volume Three is already in the planning stages and will be published in September, 1994. And look out for one or two other surprises on the Stronach front.

For further details, or if you'd just like to tell us what you thought of your book and what you'd like to see in future, we'd be delighted to hear from you.

Send an SAE to:

Alison Reid, Stronach Media Ltd., Tullynessle, Alford, Aberdeenshire, AB33 8QN

Master
Mind
Token